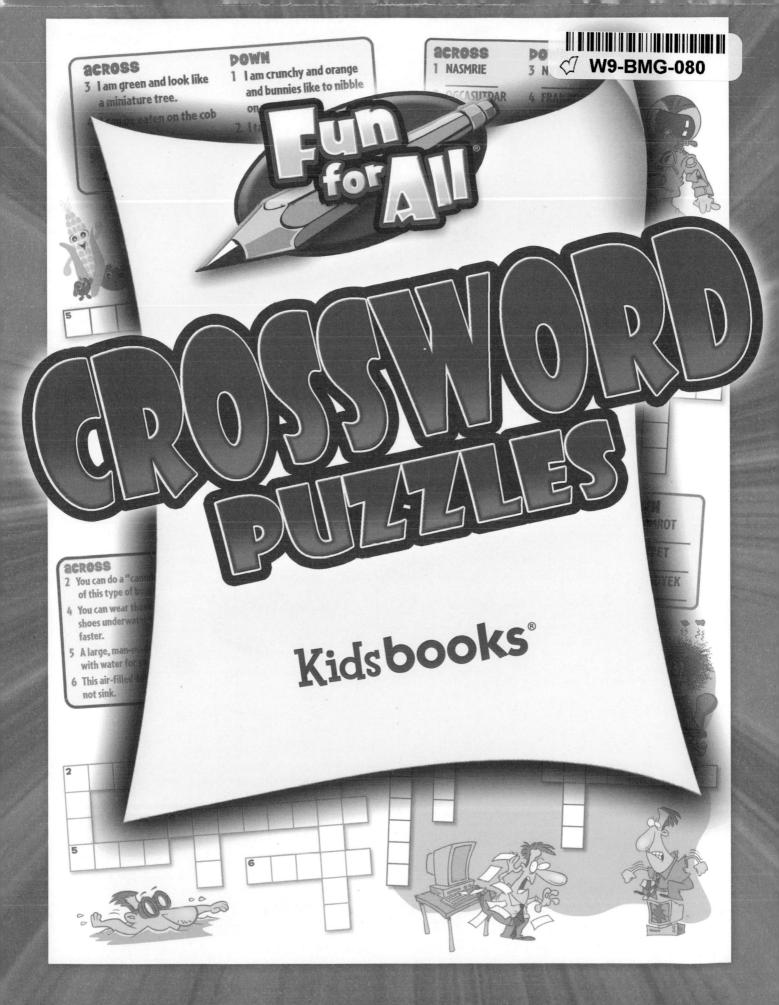

Birds of a Feather

Use the pictures below to complete this crossword puzzle.

Across

1
4
6

Down

1
2
5

Answer Page

I Love Your Shoes!

Use the clues below to complete this crossword puzzle.

ACROSS
4 Tennis _____
5 High _____
6 Fuzzy _____

DOWN
1 Mary _____
2 Soccer _____
3 Rain _____

Answer Page

ACROSS

4 Tennis _____

5 High _____

6 Fuzzy _____

DOWN

1 Mary _____

2 Soccer _____

3 Rain _____

You Were Saying

Fill in the blanks below to complete this crossword puzzle.

ACROSS
1 Grizzly _____
2 Help _____
3 License to _____
4 _____ in the shallow end.

DOWN
2 Wash and _____
3 Park closes at _____
5 _____ or not
6 Seashells on the _____

ANSWER ON BACK

Answer Page

ACROSS

1 BEARS
2 WANTED
3 DRIVE
4 SWIM

DOWN

1 BEADY
2 WAVE
3 DUSK
5 RAYS
6 SHORE

Animals

Use the clues below to complete this crossword puzzle.

ACROSS
3 Swings in a tree
4 Long neck
5 Big trunk
7 Slow moving, loves water

DOWN
1 White and furry
2 Lives in a hive
6 Striped cat
8 Big mane

ANSWER ON BACK

Answer Page

across
3 Swings in a tree
4 Long neck
5 Big trunk
7 Slow moving, loves water

DOWN
1 White and furry
2 Lives in a hive
6 Striped cat
8 Big mane

Crossword solution:

- 1 Down: POLAR BEAR
- 2 Down: BEE
- 3 Across: MONKEY
- 4 Across: GIRAFFE
- 5 Across: ELEPHANT
- 6 Down: TIGER
- 7 Across: TURTLE
- 8 Down: LION

Sensing Senses

Use the clues below to complete this crossword puzzle.

ACROSS

2 Our noses play a key part in using this sense.

3 This sense helps us to physically feel things.

DOWN

1 We use this sense when listening to music and other sounds.

2 This sense allows us to view landscapes, colors, and objects.

3 When we eat different foods, our tongues help us with this sense.

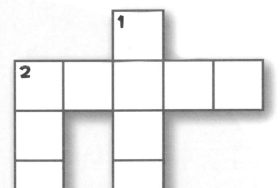

Answer Page

ACROSS

2 Our noses play a key part in using this sense.

3 This sense helps us to physically feel things.

DOWN

1 We use this sense when listening to music and other sounds.

2 This sense allows us to view landscapes, colors, and objects.

3 When we eat different foods, our tongues help us with this sense.

1 HEARING
2 SMELL
2 SIGHT
3 TOUCH
3 TASTE

Lights! Camera! Action!

Use the pictures below to complete this crossword puzzle.

ACROSS
2 3 7 9 10 MOVIE 11

DOWN
1 4 5
6 8 12

Answer Page

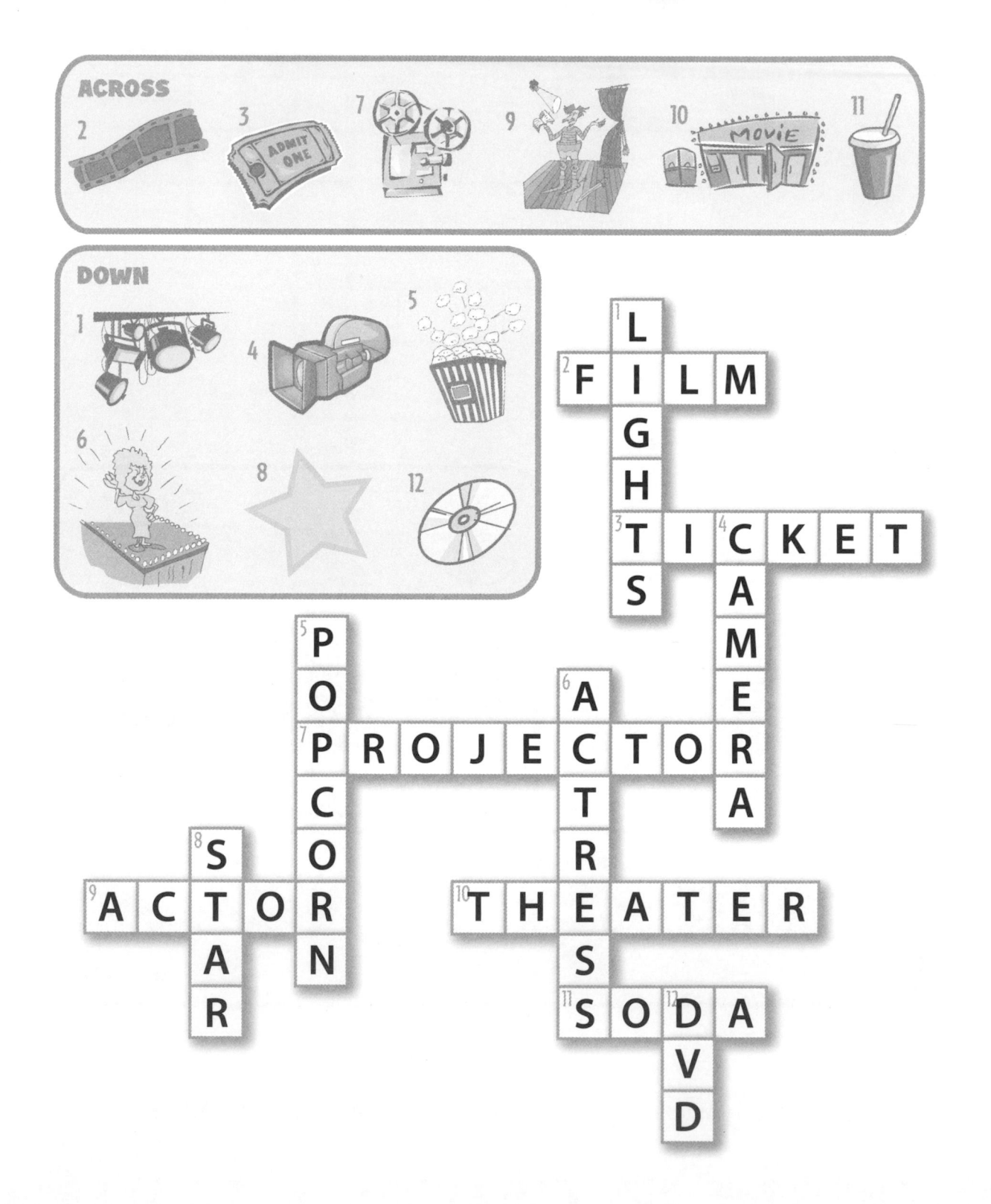

World Capitals

Put the capitals of each country in the crossword puzzle.

ACROSS
5 Italy
7 Belgium
8 Ireland
9 Austria
10 Egypt
11 United Kingdom
12 India

DOWN
1 France
2 Germany
3 United States
4 Greece
6 Spain

Answer Page

NEW DELHI

LONDON

CAIRO

VIENNA

ATHENS

BRUSSELS

DUBLIN

BERLIN

ROME

PARIS

WASHINGTON

ACROSS		DOWN	
5	Italy	1	France
7	Belgium	2	Germany
8	Ireland	3	United States
9	Austria	4	Greece
10	Egypt	6	Spain
11	United Kingdom		
12	India		

Recess

Use the clues below to complete this crossword puzzle.

ACROSS

3 In this game you must keep your balance as you jump from square to square.

5 You must pump your legs to get higher and higher when sitting on this.

DOWN

1 In this game, you must avoid getting hit by the opposing team's balls.

2 You can use this to draw on sidewalks, but if it rains, your pictures will be erased!

4 You must be quick in this game to run from the person who is "It."

5 This structure has a downward slope and is smooth so you can move fast!

Answer Page

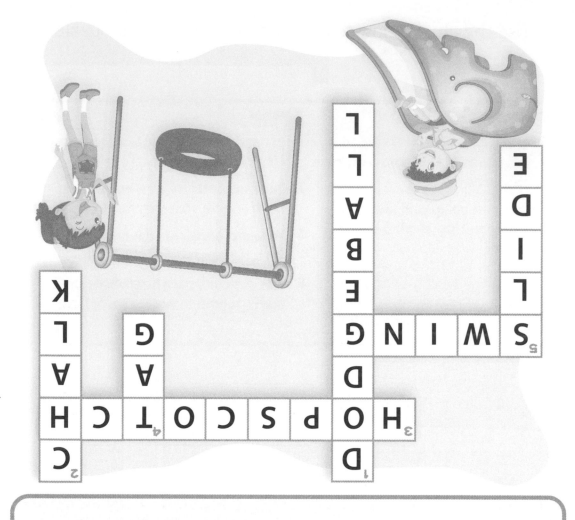

ACROSS

3 In this game you must keep your balance as you jump from square to square.

5 You must pump your legs to get higher and higher when sitting on this.

DOWN

1 In this game, you must avoid getting hit by the opposing team's balls.

2 You can use this to draw on sidewalks, but if it rains, your pictures will be erased!

4 You must be quick in this game to run from the person who is "It."

5 This structure has a downward slope and is smooth so you can move fast!

Flying Bugs

Use the clues below to complete this crossword puzzle.

across

5 This annoying little bug may leave you with itchy red bug bites.

6 Once a caterpillar, this bug has now come out of its cocoon with beautiful wings.

DOWN

1 A red bug that often has black dots on its back

2 A fuzzy yellow-and-black striped bug

3 This type of bug shares part of its name with a mythical creature that breathes fire.

4 A type of fly that is named after produce like apples, oranges, and pears

ANSWER ON BACK

Answer Page

ACROSS

5 This annoying little bug may leave you with itchy red bug bites.

6 Once a caterpillar, this bug has now come out of its cocoon with beautiful wings.

DOWN

1 A red bug that often has black dots on its back

2 A fuzzy yellow-and-black striped bug

3 This type of bug shares part of its name with a mythical creature that breathes fire.

4 A type of fly that is named after produce like apples, oranges, and pears

What Farm Animal Am I?

Use the clues below to complete this crossword puzzle.

ACROSS
2 I am fluffy and white and I say, "Bahh!"
6 I am a bird that likes to crow at dawn.

DOWN
1 I live in a coop and lay eggs.
3 I have a curly pink tail and I like to roll in mud.
4 I have a long mane and like to gallop.
5 I produce milk and I like to chew on grass.

ANSWER ON BACK

Answer Page

ACROSS

2 I am fluffy and white and I say, "Bahh!"

6 I am a bird that likes to crow at dawn.

DOWN

1 I live in a coop and lay eggs.

3 I have a curly pink tail and I like to roll in mud.

4 I have a long mane and like to gallop.

5 I produce milk and I like to chew on grass.

Crossword solution:

- 1 Down: CHICKEN
- 2 Across: SHEEP
- 3 Down: PIG
- 4 Down: HORSE
- 5 Down: COW
- 6 Across: ROOSTER

Pizza Toppings

Use the clues below to complete this crossword puzzle.

across

4 Considered part of the fungi family, these can be delicious on pizza.

5 This red, round sausage is one of the most popular pizza toppings.

6 These veggies are sweet and come in colors like green, red, yellow, and orange.

DOWN

1 Some people love these small, salty fish on their pizza.

2 Often eaten with eggs, this salty pork can be a crunchy surprise on pizza.

3 On a Hawaiian pizza, this topping accompanies ham.

ANSWER ON BACK

Answer Page

ACROSS

4 Considered part of the fungi family, these can be delicious on pizza.

5 This red, round sausage is one of the most popular pizza toppings.

6 These veggies are sweet and come in colors like green, red, yellow, and orange.

DOWN

1 Some people love these small, salty fish on their pizza.

2 Often eaten with eggs, this salty pork can be a crunchy surprise on pizza.

3 On a Hawaiian pizza, this topping accompanies ham.

Autumn

Use the clues below to complete this crossword puzzle.

ACROSS

1 The air gets ____ .
4 There is less and less _____ .
5 The trees get ____ .
6 Brightly colored leaves
7 Orange vegetables that can be carved
8 Put away light jackets, put on _____ .
10 Gathering of crops
11 The season to prepare for _____

DOWN

2 What falls in autumn
3 Light up the ____ .
6 Another name for autumn
9 Can harm delicate plants

ANSWER ON BACK

Answer Page

ACROSS

1 The air gets ___
4 There is less and less ___
5 The trees get ___
6 Brightly colored leaves
7 Orange vegetables that can be carved
8 Put away light jackets, put on ___
10 Gathering of crops
11 The season to prepare for ___

DOWN

2 What falls in autumn
3 Light up the ___
6 Another name for autumn
9 Can harm delicate plants

Grid answers:
1 CHILLY
2 LEAVES
3 FIRE
4 DAYLIGHT
5 BARE
6 FOLIAGE / FALL
7 PUMPKINS
8 WARM COATS
9 FROST
10 HARVEST
11 WINTER
ALL

Let's Play Outside

Use the clues below to complete this crossword puzzle.

DOWN

1 A small disc thrown back and forth between two people or a person and a dog.

2 Jump on this stick to bounce up and down.

3 This type of rope can be used to play Double-Dutch or simply to skip on your own.

ACROSS

4 This is a game played with two small rackets, and a "birdie."

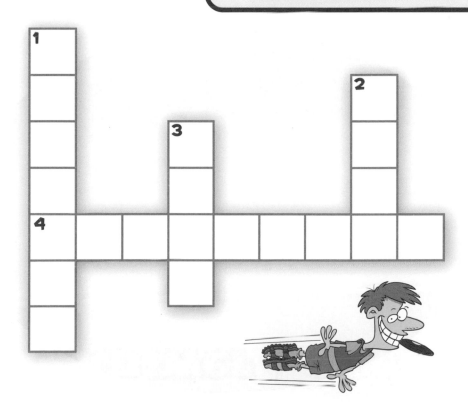

ANSWER ON BACK

Answer Page

DOWN

1 A small disc thrown back and forth between two people or a person and a dog.

2 Jump on this stick to bounce up and down.

3 This type of rope can be used to play Double-Dutch or simply to skip on your own.

ACROSS

4 This is a game played with two small rackets, and a "birdie."

Crossword solution:

- 1 (down) FRISBEE
- 2 (down) POGO
- 3 (down) JUMP
- 4 (across) BADMINTON

Black & White Animals

Use the clues below to complete this crossword puzzle.

ACROSS

3 I like to eat bamboo.

4 I live in the Antartic or South Pole and like to waddle.

5 I look like a horse with stripes.

DOWN

1 I am part of the weasel family.

2 I may be cute but don't get too close or I might spray you—P.U.!

Answer Page

ACROSS

3 I like to eat bamboo.

4 I live in the Antartic or South Pole and like to waddle.

5 I look like a horse with stripes.

DOWN

1 I am part of the weasel family.

2 I may be cute but don't get too close or I might spray you—P.U.!

State Birds

Put the state bird of each state in the crossword puzzle.

ACROSS
3 Michigan
6 Iowa
8 California
11 New Mexico
12 Vermont

DOWN
1 Maryland
2 Tennessee
4 Colorado
5 New York
7 Indiana
9 Georgia
10 Arizona

ANSWER ON BACK

Answer Page

ACROSS
3 Michigan
6 Iowa
8 California
11 New Mexico
12 Vermont

DOWN
1 Maryland
2 Tennessee
4 Colorado
5 New York
7 Indiana
9 Georgia
10 Arizona

Let's Go to the Beach

Use the pictures below to complete this crossword puzzle.

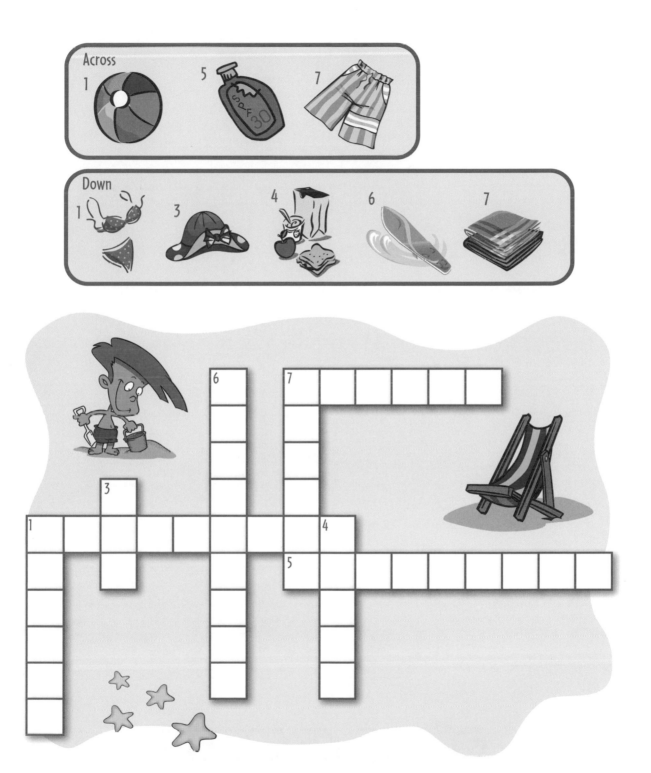

Across

1   5   7

Down

1   3   4   6   7

Answer Page

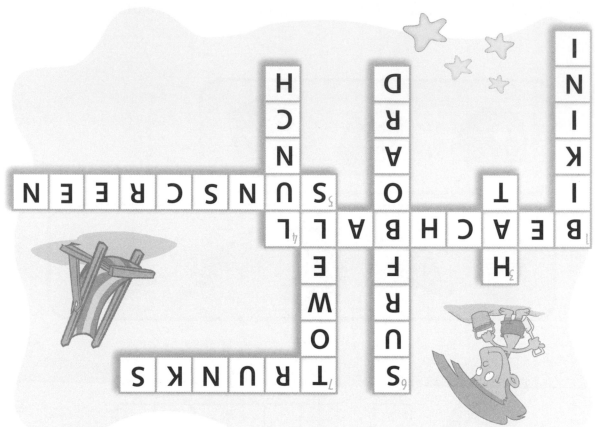

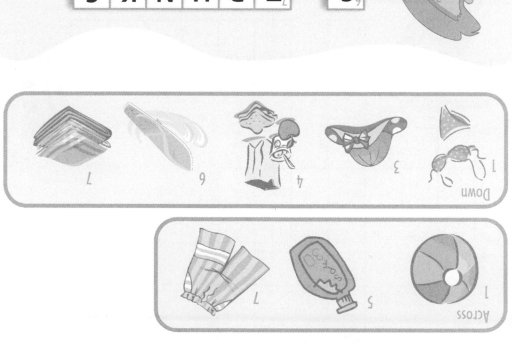

Some European Countries

Use the clues below to complete this crossword puzzle.

ACROSS

2 In this country, you can run with the bulls.

5 This country is home to the Eiffel Tower.

6 This country is known for its delicious pasta and pizza.

7 This country is known as the birthplace of Mozart.

DOWN

1 This is the country where golf was invented.

3 Consider yourself lucky if you find a four-leaf clover in this green country.

4 Athens is the capital of this country.

ANSWER ON BACK

Answer Page

ACROSS

2 In this country, you can run with the bulls.

5 This country is home to the Eiffel Tower.

6 This country is known for its delicious pasta and pizza.

7 This country is known as the birthplace of Mozart.

DOWN

1 This is the country where golf was invented.

3 Consider yourself lucky if you find a four-leaf clover in this green country.

4 Athens is the capital of this country.

1 SCOTLAND
2 SPAIN
3 IRELAND
4 GREECE
5 FRANCE
6 ITALY
7 AUSTRIA

Colors

Use the clues below to complete this crossword puzzle.

ACROSS

4 The sky is this color on a clear day.

5 Grass is this color when it gets a lot of water and sunshine.

6 Some daffodils and buttercups are this color.

DOWN

1 This is the color of marshmallows.

2 Basketballs are this color.

3 This color means STOP or DANGER.

4 Leaves that don't get enough water or nutrients turn this color.

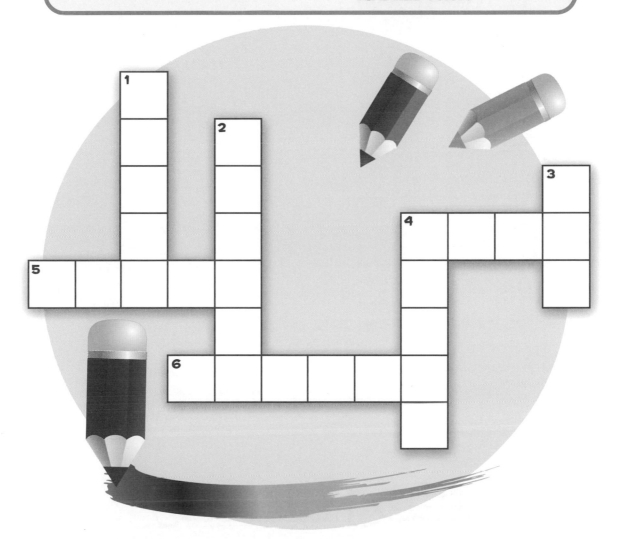

ANSWER ON BACK

Answer Page

ACROSS

4 The sky is this color on a clear day.

5 Grass is this color when it gets a lot of water and sunshine.

6 Some daffodils and buttercups are this color.

DOWN

1 This is the color of marshmallows.

2 Basketballs are this color.

3 This color means STOP or DANGER.

4 Leaves that don't get enough water or nutrients turn this color.

Safety First

Use the clues below to complete this crossword puzzle.

ACROSS

2 Wear this to protect your teeth while playing contact sports

4 Wear this on your head to keep it protected

DOWN

1 Wearing these will prevent your knees, wrists and elbows from getting bruised when you fall.

3 These protective covers keep your eyes safe during sports.

Answer Page

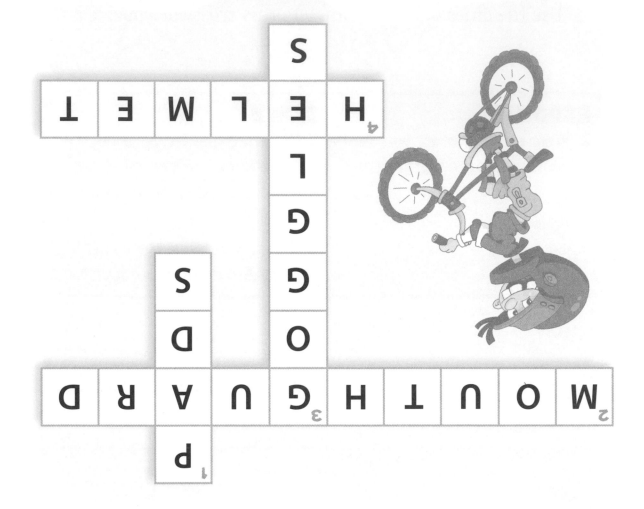

ACROSS

2 Wear this to protect your teeth while playing contact sports

4 Wear this on your head to keep it protected

DOWN

1 Wearing these will prevent your knees, wrists and elbows from getting bruised when you fall.

3 These protective covers keep your eyes safe during sports.

Relationships

Use the pictures below to complete this crossword puzzle.

Answer Page

Let's Have a Picnic

Use the clues below to complete this crossword puzzle.

across

3 Meats and cheeses placed between two pieces of bread

4 This is something you spread out on the ground and sit on.

5 You don't want to see any of these little black insects crawling around on your food.

DOWN

1 This yellow drink is sweet as long as you don't forget to add the sugar!

2 All of your picnic food can be put in this object and carried.

Answer Page

ACROSS

3 Meats and cheeses placed between two pieces of bread

4 This is something you spread out on the ground and sit on.

5 You don't want to see any of these little black insects crawling around on your food.

DOWN

1 This yellow drink is sweet as long as you don't forget to add the sugar!

2 All of your picnic food can be put in this object and carried.

Opposites Attract

First figure out the antonym of each word written below.
Then place it in its spot in the crossword puzzle.

ACROSS
1 Old _____
2 Cold _____
3 White _____

DOWN
2 Light _____
3 Good _____
4 Dry _____

ANSWER ON BACK

Answer Page

across
1 Old _____
2 Cold _____
3 White _____

DOWN
2 Light _____
3 Good _____
4 Dry _____

	¹N	E	⁴W	
			E	
	²H	O	T	
	E			
³B	L	A	C	K
A		V		
D		Y		

Traveling Techniques

Use the clues below to complete this crossword puzzle.

ACROSS

2 This vehicle has four wheels and is the most common way to travel.

3 This is a common way to travel to places across the ocean.

5 You can find these yellow cars in cities, but you must pay the driver to take you to your destination.

6 This vehicle has wings and can fly through the air at very high speeds.

DOWN

1 This flying vehicle has a giant propeller that helps it gain speed and height.

3 You can ride in this form of transportation across long distances and even to school!

4 This form of transportation moves along tracks.

ANSWER ON BACK

Answer Page

ACROSS

2 This vehicle has four wheels and is the most common way to travel.

3 This is a common way to travel to places across the ocean.

5 You can find these yellow cars in cities, but you must pay the driver to take you to your destination.

6 This vehicle has wings and can fly through the air at very high speeds.

DOWN

1 This flying vehicle has a giant propeller that helps it gain speed and height.

3 You can ride in this form of transportation across long distances and even to school!

4 This form of transportation moves along tracks.

Hot Drinks

Use the clues below to complete this crossword puzzle.

ACROSS

3 After playing in the snow I like to have marshmallows in my hot _____.

4 In the fall, I like to pick pumpkins while drinking some apple _____.

DOWN

1 In the morning, if my mom and dad are tired, they will drink a cup of _____.

2 I like to have honey and lemon in my _____.

Answer Page

across

3 After playing in the snow
I like to have marshmallows
in my hot _____.

4 In the fall, I like to pick
pumpkins while drinking
some apple _____.

down

1 In the morning, if my mom
and dad are tired, they will
drink a cup of _____.

2 I like to have honey and
lemon in my _____.

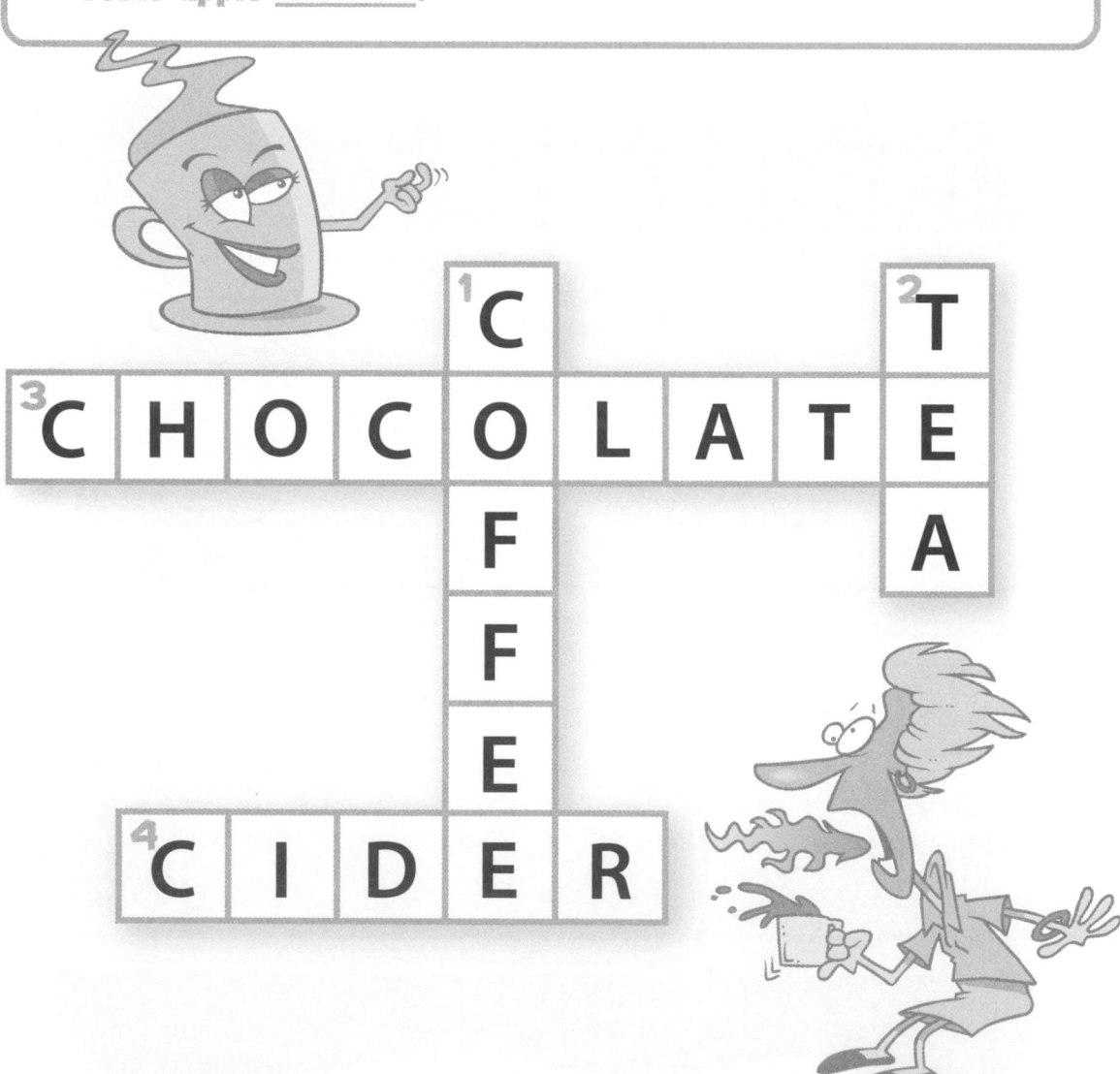

In the Kitchen

Use the clues below to complete this crossword puzzle.

ACROSS

3 Quickly reheat any food inside of me by hitting the start button.

7 I keep all of your food cold and fresh so that it doesn't spoil.

DOWN

1 I can transform plain bread into a warm and crusty breakfast food.

2 Put dirty plates and silverware in me and they will come out sparkling clean.

4 You can bake cookies inside of me.

5 Place a pan or teakettle on top of me to cook soup or boil water.

6 Wash your hands in me before your eat and remember to use soap!

ANSWER ON BACK

Answer Page

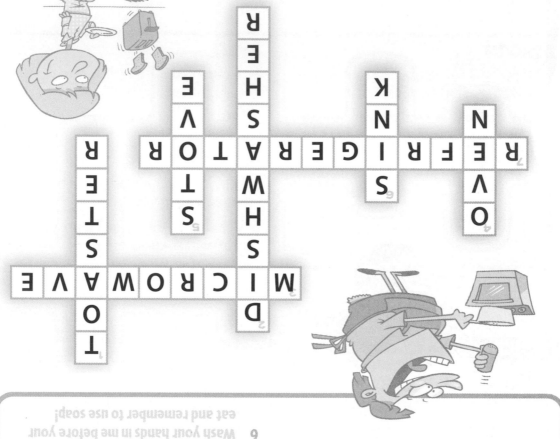

ACROSS

3. Quickly reheat any food inside of me by hitting the start button.

7. I keep all of your food cold and fresh so that it doesn't spoil.

DOWN

1. I can transform plain bread into a warm and crusty breakfast food.

2. Put dirty plates and silverware in me and they will come out sparkling clean.

4. You can bake cookies inside of me.

5. Place a pan or teakettle on top of me to cook soup or boil water.

6. Wash your hands in me before your eat and remember to use soap!

State Capitals

Put the capital of each state in the crossword puzzle.

ACROSS

1 Oregon
2 West Virginia
3 Idaho
4 New Jersey
5 Rhode Island

DOWN

1 New Mexico
6 Wisconsin
7 Tennessee

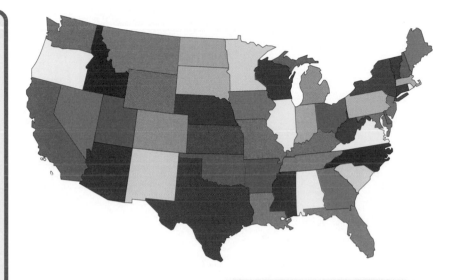

ANSWER ON BACK

ACROSS
1 Oregon
2 West Virginia
3 Idaho
4 New Jersey
5 Rhode Island

DOWN
1 New Mexico
6 Wisconsin
7 Tennessee

Crossword solution:

¹SALEM
²CHARLESTON
³BOISE
⁴TRENTON
⁵PROVIDENCE
⁶MADISON
⁷NASHVILLE
SANTAFE

Ready for Takeoff

Use the clues below to complete this crossword puzzle.

ACROSS
1 Rest your head
3 Lean against
7 Really fast plane
8 Put your food on
10 Where the pilot sits
11 Serves the food

DOWN
1 Get on board the ___
2 Provides the power
4 What the pilots operate
5 Keeps you strapped in
6 It floats
9 Flies the plane

ANSWER ON BACK

Answer Page

Let's Bake a Cake

Use the clues below to complete this crossword puzzle.

ACROSS

3 A machine that blends all the ingredients together

6 Put the uncooked cake in this heated appliance to watch the cake rise!

7 This is what makes the cake taste sweet.

DOWN

1 A slick liquid that helps the batter ingredients stick together and makes a cake moist.

2 Also known as icing, this smooth topping covers the whole cake.

4 This powdery substance is a key ingredient in cake batter.

5 These oval ingredients help the cake rise.

ANSWER ON BACK

Answer Page

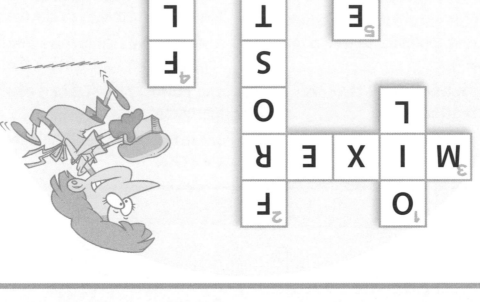

ACROSS

3 A machine that blends all the ingredients together

6 Put the uncooked cake in this heated appliance to watch the cake rise!

7 This is what makes the cake taste sweet.

DOWN

1 A slick liquid that helps the batter ingredients stick together and makes a cake moist.

2 Also known as icing, this smooth topping covers the whole cake.

4 This powdery substance is a key ingredient in cake batter.

5 These oval ingredients help the cake rise.

Rhyme Time

Find a word that rhymes with each word listed below, using the clues in the parentheses. Then read down the column in blue to answer the question:

"What rhymes with 'orange'?"

1) SEA (body part) _____

2) HOWL (garden tool) _____

3) FIRST (explode) _____

4) HARP (pointy) _____

5) HEIGHT (chew) _____

6) FROWN (funny guy) _____

7) SPONGE (fall) _____

Answer Page

NOTHING rhymes with orange.

Crossword grid answers:

1. KNEE
2. TROWEL
3. BURST
4. SHARP
5. BITE
6. CLOWN
7. PLUNGE

1) SEA (body part) _____

2) HOWL (garden tool) _____

3) FIRST (explode) _____

4) HARP (pointy) _____

5) HEIGHT (chew) _____

6) FROWN (funny guy) _____

7) SPONGE (fall) _____

Add It Up

Use the clues below to complete this crossword puzzle.

across
1 9 + 8 =
2 18 + 11 =

DOWN
1 24 + 36 =
3 16 + 24 =

ANSWER ON BACK

Answer Page

Musical Types

Use the clues below to complete this crossword puzzle.

ACROSS
1 Singers perform
6 Music only, no voices
8 ___ and roll
9 Classical singers
10 From all over the globe

DOWN
2 Symphony orchestra
3 Acoustic guitar with lyrics
4 ___-hop
5 Mix of rock and jazz
7 Swings

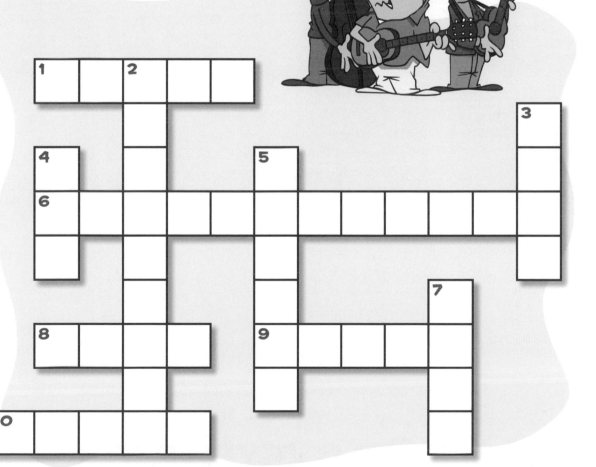

ANSWER ON BACK

Answer Page

ACROSS

1 Singers perform
6 Music only, no voices
8 ____ and roll
9 Classical singers
10 From all over the globe

DOWN

2 Symphony orchestra
3 Acoustic guitar with lyrics
4 ____-hop
5 Mix of rock and jazz
7 Swings

What Tool Am I?

Use the clues below to complete this crossword puzzle.

ACROSS

2 I am a short metal object that helps keep wooden planks together.

4 I help twist screws into place.

6 I am used to determine or adjust something horizontally.

DOWN

1 I bang nails into wood.

3 I use my sharp teeth to cut wood in half.

5 I make holes in wood and other hard substances.

Answer Page

ACROSS

2 I am a short metal object that helps keep wooden planks together.

4 I help twist screws into place.

6 I am used to determine or adjust something horizontally.

DOWN

1 I bang nails into wood.

3 I use my sharp teeth to cut wood in half.

5 I make holes in wood and other hard substances.

Where's the Party?

Unscramble these types of parties on the blanks below and then place them in this crossword puzzle.

ACROSS
1 NVREIANRYAS
_____

2 PTMSIBA
_____

3 TEWES XSIEETN
_____

4 RAB TVHMIAZ
_____

DOWN
5 DWEDGIN
_____

6 TRHDBIYA
_____

7 DUATAGNROI
_____

8 MERETIERTN
_____

Answer Page

across

1 NVREIANRYAS

2 PTMSIBA

3 TEWES XSIEETN

4 RAB TVHMIAZ

DOWN

5 DWEDGIN

6 TRHDBIYA

7 DUATAGNROI

8 MERETIERTN

[7]G
[1]A N N I V E R S A R Y
[8]R
[2]B A P T I S M
[5]W [6]B
[3]S W E E T S I X T E E N

Sauces

Put the sauce that goes with each of these foods...

ACROSS
1 Eggs
2 Ribs
3 Hot wings

DOWN
4 Pasta
5 Turkey
6 Tortilla chips

ANSWER ON BACK

Answer Page

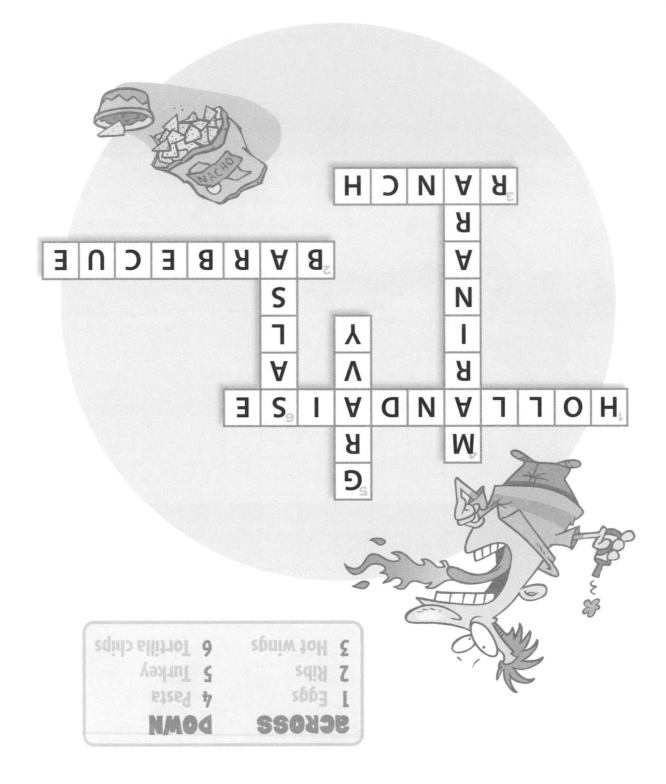

ACROSS	**DOWN**
1 Eggs	4 Pasta
2 Ribs	5 Turkey
3 Hot wings	6 Tortilla chips

1 HOLLANDAISE
2 BARBECUE
3 RANCH
4 MARINARA
5 GRAVY
6 SALSA

NACHO

Back to School

Use the clues below to complete this crossword puzzle.

ACROSS

6 If you make a mistake when writing, you can use this gummy pink object to fix it.

7 You can use this to measure or draw straight lines.

9 A three-ringed object that holds all of your papers

10 This sharp object helps you cut paper.

12 You can keep all of your school supplies in this sack and carry it on one or both shoulders.

13 This electronic device can solve math equations.

14 If your pencil is dull, use this to make it pointier.

DOWN

1 This white sticky substance helps keep things together.

2 You often use these to color pictures or make posters.

3 This spiral bound object has lined paper and is where you would write notes.

4 Use this yellow marker to mark important words or sentences while reading.

5 This rectangular object has two pockets in which to store your papers.

8 A number 2 lead–tipped writing utensil

11 A strip of clear material that helps you stick things together.

Answer Page

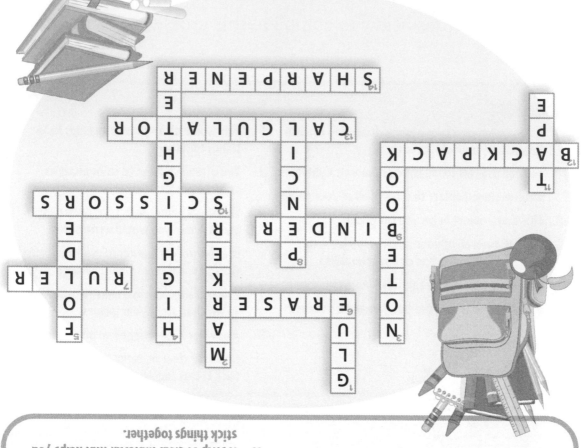

ACROSS

6 If you make a mistake when writing, you can use this gummy pink object to fix it.

7 You can use this to measure or draw straight lines.

9 A three-ringed object that holds all of your papers

10 This sharp object helps you cut paper.

12 You can keep all of your school supplies in this sack and carry it on one or both shoulders.

13 This electronic device can solve math equations.

14 If your pencil is dull, use this to make it pointier.

DOWN

1 This white sticky substance helps keep things together.

2 You often use these to color pictures or make posters.

3 This spiral bound object has lined paper and is where you would write notes.

4 Use this yellow marker to mark important words or sentences while reading.

5 This rectangular object has two pockets in which to store your papers.

8 A number 2 lead-tipped writing utensil

11 A strip of clear material that helps you stick things together.

Winter Wonderland

Use the pictures below to complete this crossword puzzle.

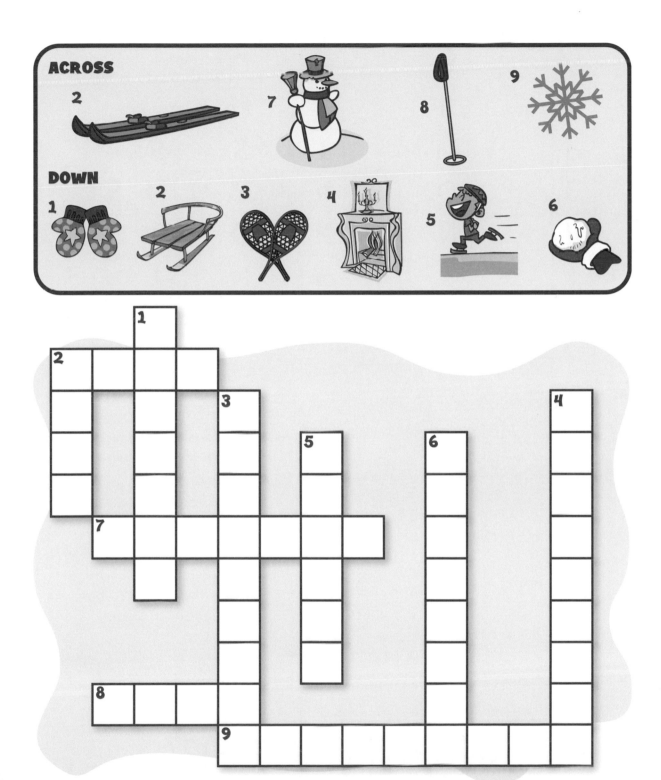

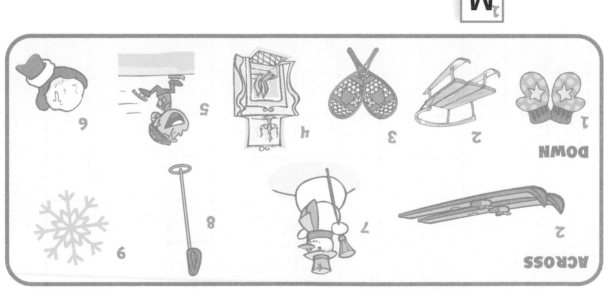

Answer Page

ACROSS

DOWN

SNOWFLAKE
FIREPLACE
SNOWMOBILE
SNOWMAN
SKATER
SNOWSHOES
POLE
MITTENS
SKIS
SLED

Authors

Write these famous authors' first names in the blanks below and then complete this crossword puzzle.

ACROSS
1 ____ Christian Anderson
2 ____ Kipling
3 ____ Dickens
4 ____ Shelley
5 ____ Austen

DOWN
1 ____ Melville
2 ____ Waldo Emerson
5 ____ London
6 ____ Carroll
7 ____ Hodgson Burnett

Answer Page

ACROSS

1 _____ Christian Anderson
2 _____ Kipling
3 _____ Dickens
4 _____ Shelley
5 _____ Austen

DOWN

1 _____ Melville
2 _____ Waldo Emerson
5 _____ London
6 _____ Carroll
7 _____ Hodgson Burnett

Ice-Cream Sundae

Use the clues below to complete this crossword puzzle.

ACROSS

2 Put one of these small, red fruits on top of your sundae to make it complete.

4 This sweet golden syrup tastes a lot like butterscotch.

5 Add this to make your sundae a split!

6 This is a type of hot chocolate syrup you drizzle on your sundae.

DOWN

1 This type of cream goes great on top.

3 You may choose between the rainbow or chocolate variety of these.

Answer Page

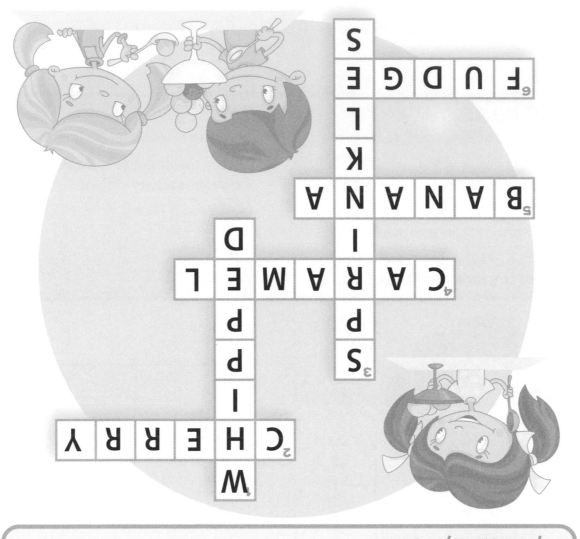

ACROSS

2   Put one of these small, red fruits on top of your sundae to make it complete.

4   This sweet golden syrup tastes a lot like butterscotch.

5   Add this to make your sundae a split!

6   This is a type of hot chocolate syrup you drizzle on your sundae.

DOWN

1   This type of cream goes great on top.

3   You may choose between the rainbow or chocolate variety of these.

Brush Your Teeth

Use the clues below to complete this crossword puzzle.

ACROSS

2 _____ is a minty gel or paste that helps clean and polish your teeth.

4 You use a _____ to scrub your teeth.

DOWN

1 Rinse with_____ to leave your breath fresh.

3 Use _____ to clean in between your teeth.

ANSWER ON BACK

Answer Page

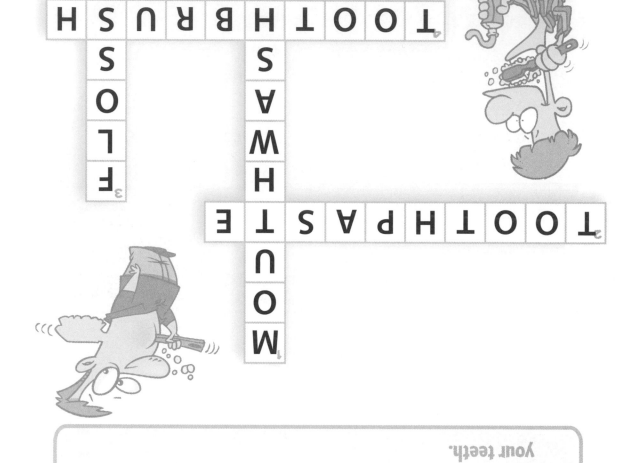

ACROSS

2 _____ is a minty gel or paste that helps clean and polish your teeth.

4 You use a _____ to scrub your teeth.

DOWN

1 Rinse with _____ to leave your breath fresh.

3 Use _____ to clean in between your teeth.

Grid answers:

- ¹ TOOTHPASTE
- ⁴ TOOTHBRUSH
- ¹ MOUTHWASH
- ³ FLOSS
- MOUTH

How Are You Feeling?

Use the clues below to complete this crossword puzzle.

across
1 Feeling great
3 I need to cool off.
4 Let's eat!
6 Thrilled
7 Ready for a nap

DOWN
2 I'm so mad!
3 Anxious
5 A bit blue

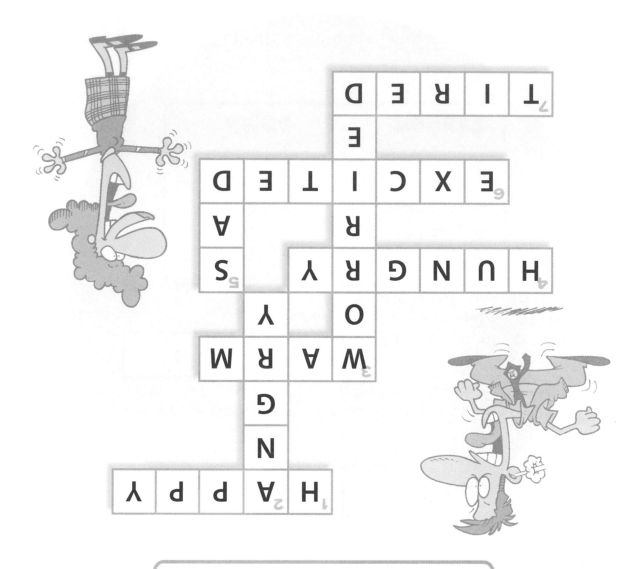

Answer Page

ACROSS

1 Feeling great
3 I need to cool off.
4 Let's eat!
6 Thrilled
7 Ready for a nap

DOWN

2 I'm so mad!
3 Anxious
5 A bit blue

Getting Dressed

Put the clothing item that goes with each body part in the crossword puzzle below.

ACROSS
1 Head
2 Chest
3 Body
4 Hands

DOWN
2 Feet
5 Legs

ANSWER ON BACK

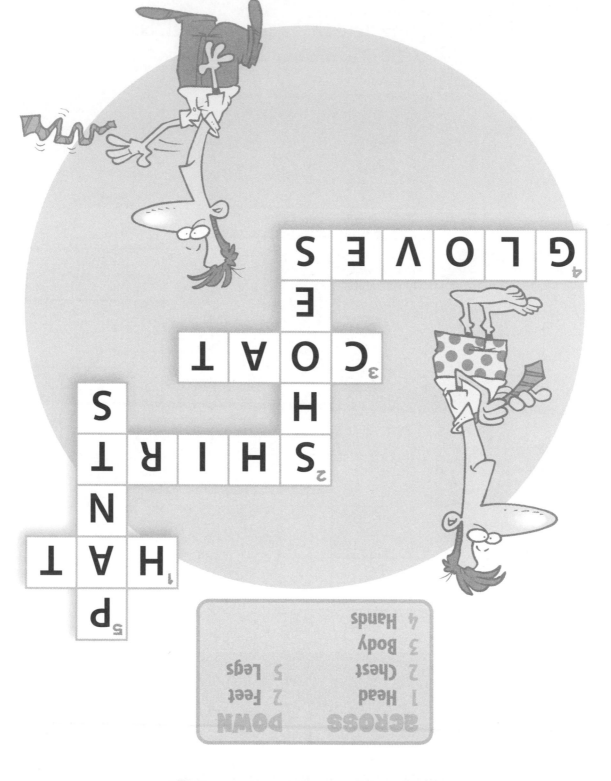

⁴GLOVES

³COAT

²SHIRT

SHOES

¹HAT

⁵PANTS

ACROSS
1 Head
2 Chest
3 Body
4 Hands

DOWN
2 Feet
5 Legs

Around the World!

Put the ethnicity of each food item in the crossword puzzle below.

ACROSS
1 Gnocchi
2 Sushi
3 Enchilada

DOWN
4 Moo shu
5 Jerk chicken
6 Tandoori chicken
7 Coq au vin
8 Ropa vieja

Answer Page

ACROSS
1 Gnocchi
2 Sushi
3 Enchilada

DOWN
4 Moo shu
5 Jerk chicken
6 Tandoori chicken
7 Coq au vin
8 Ropa vieja

1 ITALIAN
2 JAPANESE
3 MEXICAN
4 CHINESE
5 JAMAICAN
6 INDIAN
7 FRENCH
8 CUBAN

Enviromental Awareness

Use the clues below to complete this crossword puzzle.

ACROSS

3 Be sure to turn off the faucet while brushing your teeth so you don't waste this liquid.

4 Plants and flowers can be grown all year long in this glass structure.

DOWN

1 You'll want to separate plastics, papers, and glass when you do this.

2 This color represents keeping our environment clean and fresh!

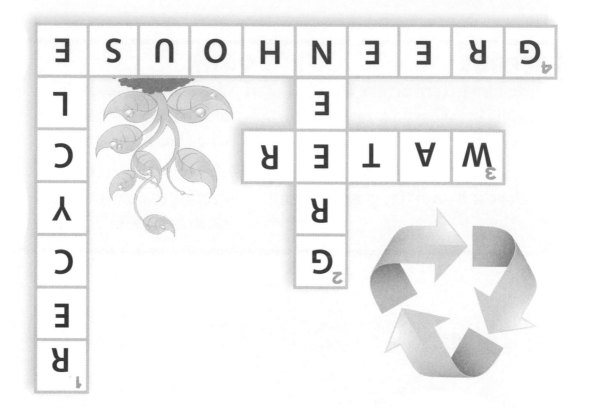

Answer Page

ACROSS

3 Be sure to turn off the faucet while brushing your teeth so you don't waste this liquid.

4 Plants and flowers can be grown all year long in this glass structure.

DOWN

1 You'll want to separate plastics, papers, and glass when you do this.

2 This color represents keeping our environment clean and fresh!

Parts of a Book

Use the clues below to complete this crossword puzzle.

ACROSS

3 Some books are divided into these and usually given a name or number.

5 This is the name of the book.

DOWN

1 The person who wrote the book is called this.

2 All traditional books have these pieces of paper in them.

4 This is the part of a book that can be seen on a bookshelf.

Answer Page

More State Capitals

Put the capital of each state in the crossword puzzle below.

ACROSS
1 Kansas
2 Illinois
3 North Carolina

DOWN
4 Massachusetts
5 South Dakota
6 Vermont
7 Arizona
8 Colorado

Answer Page

ACROSS
1 Kansas
2 Illinois
3 North Carolina

DOWN
4 Massachusetts
5 South Dakota
6 Vermont
7 Arizona
8 Colorado

1 TOPEKA
2 SPRINGFIELD
3 RALEIGH
4 BOSTON
5 PIERRE
6 MONTPELIER
7 PHOENIX
8 DENVER

Face the Music

Use the pictures below to complete this crossword puzzle.

Answer Page

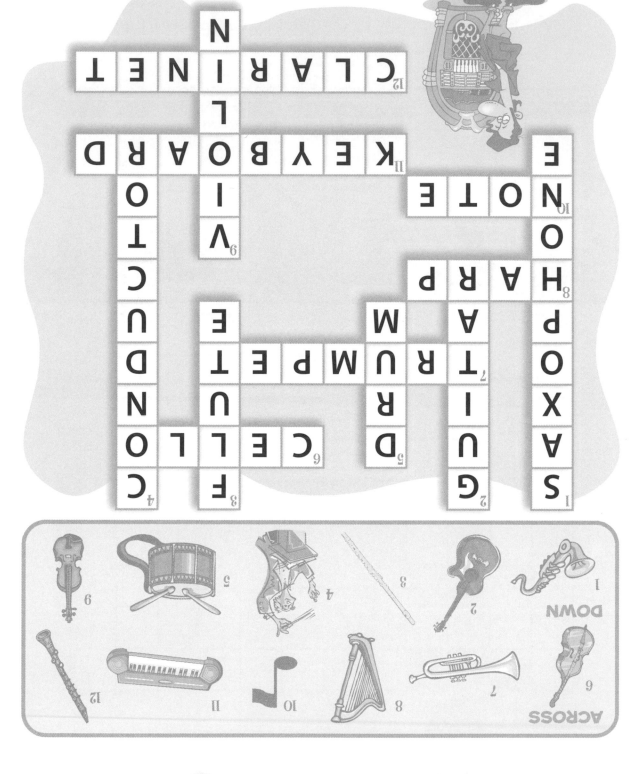

ACROSS

DOWN

Types of Salad

Use the clues below to complete this crossword puzzle.

ACROSS

1 This salad gets its name from the way its ingredients are cut.

2 Named after a Roman ruler, this salad comes with croutons and sometimes anchovies.

3 This salad is made with white flaky fish and mayonnaise.

DOWN

4 A warm bacon dressing is often served over this type of salad.

5 This salad includes feta cheese, olives, and peppers.

6 Apples, grapes, strawberries, and pineapple are some of the ingredients that make up this salad.

Answer Page

ACROSS

1 This salad gets its name from the way its ingredients are cut.

2 Named after a Roman ruler, this salad comes with croutons and sometimes anchovies.

3 This salad is made with white flaky fish and mayonnaise.

DOWN

4 A warm bacon dressing is often served over this type of salad.

5 This salad includes feta cheese, olives, and peppers.

6 Apples, grapes, strawberries, and pineapple are some of the ingredients that make up this salad.

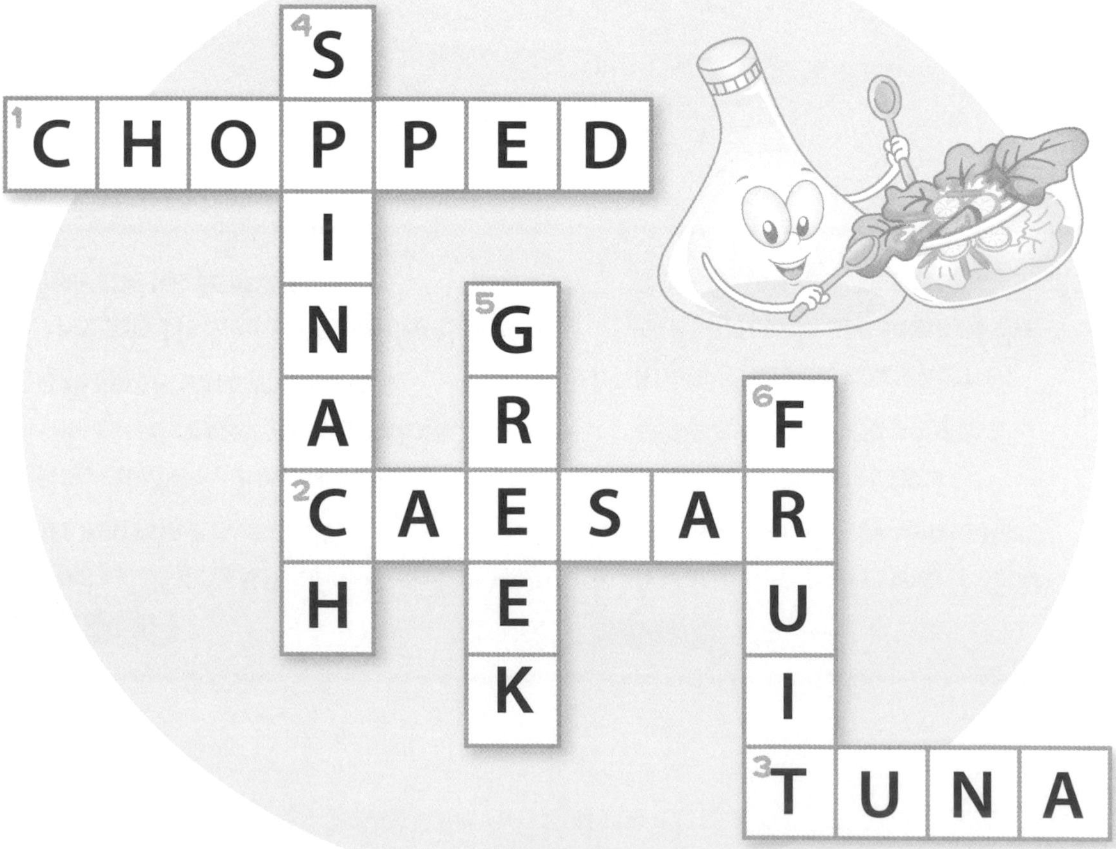

1 CHOPPED
2 CAESAR
3 TUNA
4 SPINACH
5 GREEK
6 FRUIT

Flying Machines

Use the clues to complete this crossword puzzle.

ACROSS
1 Presidential
2 Outer space
3 Wright brothers
4 Commercial airliner
5 Lands on water

DOWN
6 Hot air
7 Rotors
8 Silent military

Answer Page

across
1. Presidential
2. Outer space
3. Wright brothers
4. Commercial airliner
5. Lands on water

DOWN
6. Hot air
7. Rotors
8. Silent military

1. AIRFORCEONE
2. SHUTTLE
3. BIPLANE
4. JETPLANE
5. SEAPLANE
6. BALLOON
7. HELICOPTER
8. STEALTH

Barbecue

Use the clues to complete this crossword puzzle.

ACROSS

3 This yellow vegetable tastes great with melted butter.

4 This round beef patty is sometimes prepared with melted cheese.

DOWN

1 This shredded cabbage-based salad is made with mayonnaise.

2 This savory meat come in racks and is covered with barbecue sauce.

Answer Page

ACROSS

3 This yellow vegetable tastes great with melted butter.

4 This round beef patty is sometimes prepared with melted cheese.

DOWN

1 This shredded cabbage-based salad is made with mayonnaise.

2 This savory meat come in racks and is covered with barbecue sauce.

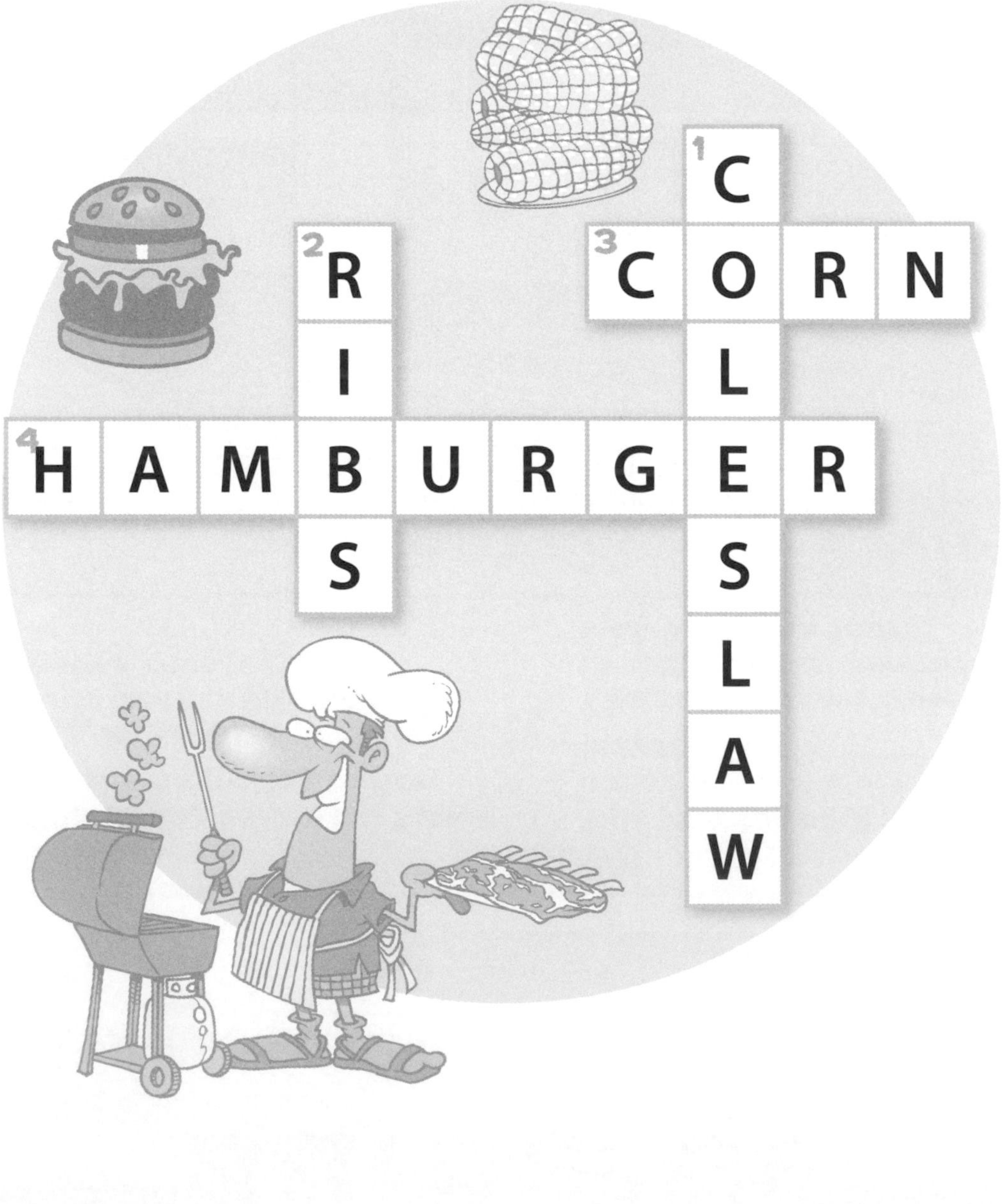

1 COLESLAW
2 RIBS
3 CORN
4 HAMBURGER

What Part of a House Am I?

Use the clues to complete this crossword puzzle.

ACROSS

2 You must open me to get inside your house, but don't forget to lock me when you leave!

3 I am a separate structure that stores your cars, bikes, and outside toys.

DOWN

1 I am made of glass and I allow you to look outside from inside.

4 I cover the top of the house to keep rain, wind, and snow out.

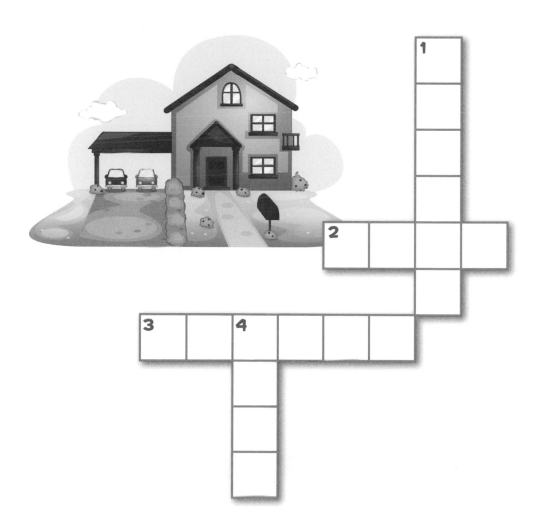

ANSWER ON BACK

Answer Page

ACROSS

2 You must open me to get inside your house, but don't forget to lock me when you leave!

3 I am a separate structure that stores your cars, bikes, and outside toys.

DOWN

1 I am made of glass and I allow you to look outside from inside.

4 I cover the top of the house to keep rain, wind, and snow out.

Extreme Sports

Use the pictures below to complete this crossword puzzle.

ANSWER ON BACK

Answer Page

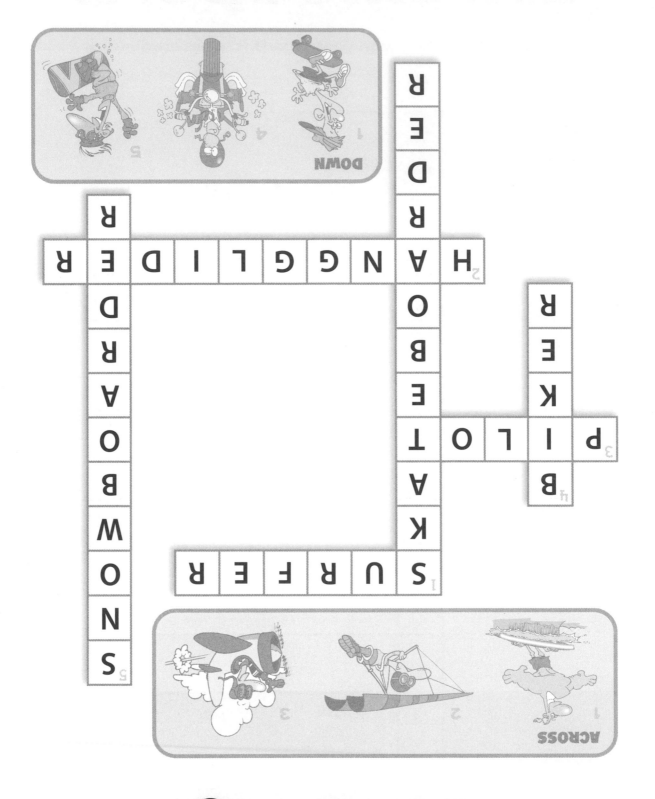

ACROSS

1. SURFER
2. HANGGLIDER
3. PILOT
4. BIKER
5. SNOWBOARDER

DOWN

1. SKATEBOARDER
2. HANGGLIDER

Deep Sleep

Use the clues to complete this crossword puzzle.

ACROSS

4 This is the room where you sleep.

5 Someone else doing this may interrupt your sleep.

DOWN

1 Lay this over yourself to keep warm.

2 This is a rectangular pad with springs designed to give you a comfortable, good night's sleep.

3 Rest your head on this.

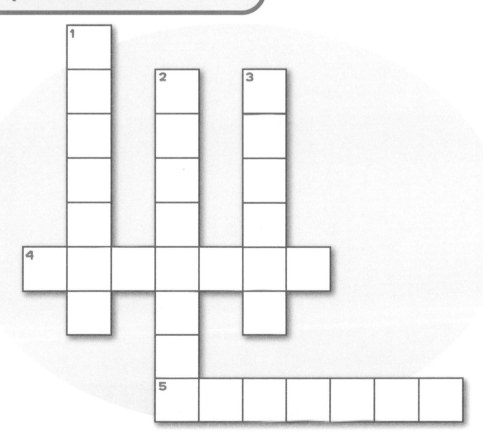

ANSWER ON BACK

Answer Page

acROSS

4 This is the room where you sleep.

5 Someone else doing this may interrupt your sleep.

DOWN

1 Lay this over yourself to keep warm.

2 This is a rectangular pad with springs designed to give you a comfortable, good night's sleep.

3 Rest your head on this.

```
¹B
 L      ²M        ³P
 A       A         I
 N       T         L
 K       T         L
⁴B E D R O O M
 T       E         W
         S
        ⁵S N O R I N G
```

Scrumptious State Favorites

Use the clues to complete this crossword puzzle.

ACROSS

1 You will need a mallet to crack open these Maryland favorites, but be careful of the claws!

5 This small, dark or golden dried fruit is a favorite in California.

6 Bostonians love this baked or refried fiber-filled food so much, the city is nicknamed for it.

7 These small sea critters with antenna are a favorite in Louisiana.

DOWN

2 This red meat is a Texas favorite.

3 The state of Maine has some of the freshest of this red shellfish.

4 This dairy product is well-loved in Wisconsin.

Answer Page

across
1 You will need a mallet to crack open these Maryland favorites, but be careful of the claws!

5 This small, dark or golden dried fruit is a favorite in California.

6 Bostonians love this baked or refried fiber-filled food so much, the city is nicknamed for it.

7 These small sea critters with antenna are a favorite in Louisiana.

DOWN
2 This red meat is a Texas favorite.

3 The state of Maine has some of the freshest of this red shellfish.

4 This dairy product is well-loved in Wisconsin.

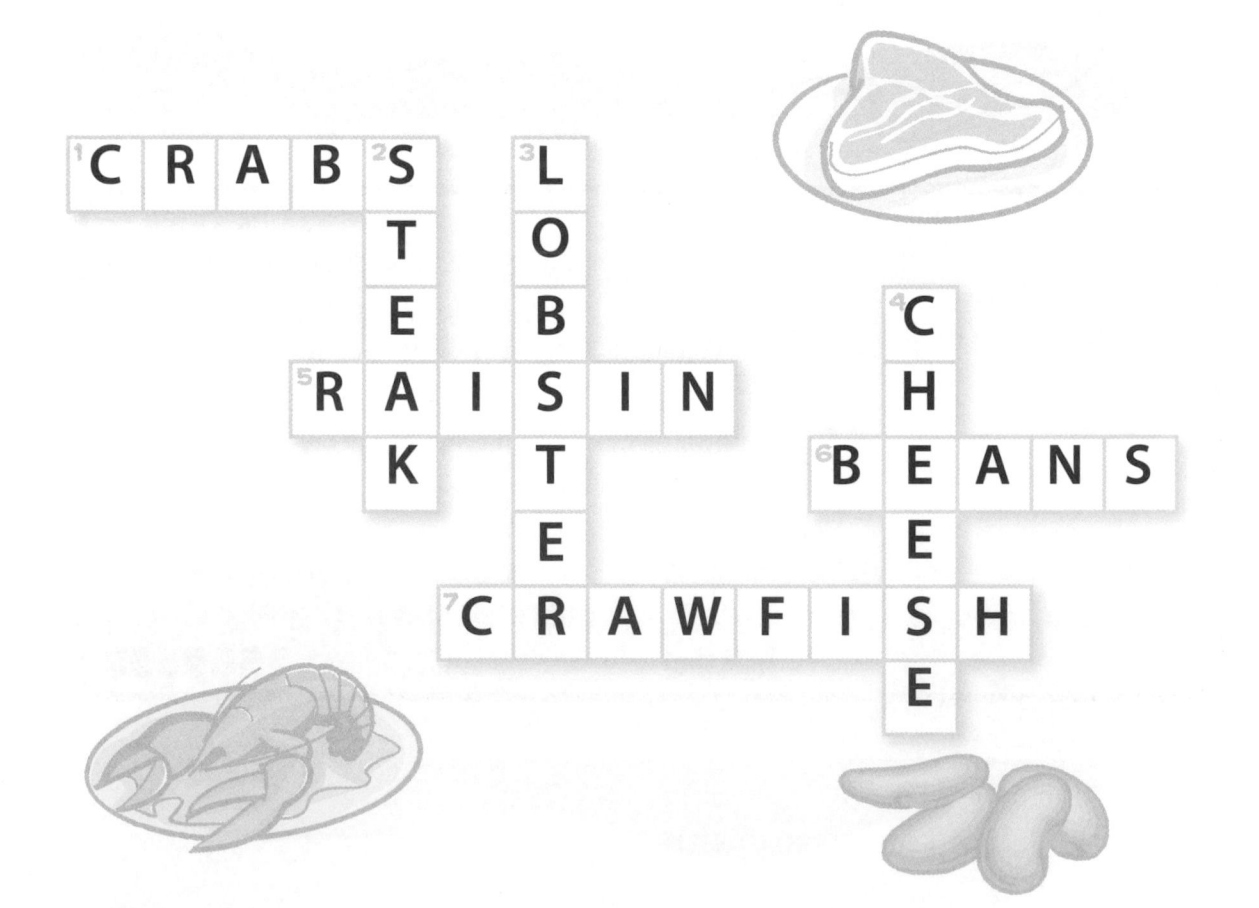

At the Grocery Store

Use the clues to complete this crossword puzzle.

across

5 I am another name for a grocery store.

DOWN

1 You put your groceries inside of us as you check out.

2 You need me to pay for your food.

3 I am the person who will ring up your groceries.

4 Put your groceries in me as you wheel me along the aisles.

Answer Page

SUPERMARKET
MONEY
CASH
CART
BAGS

ACROSS

5 I am another name for a grocery store.

DOWN

1 You put your groceries inside of us as you check out.

2 You need me to pay for your food.

3 I am the person who will ring up your groceries.

4 Put your groceries in me as you wheel me along the aisles.

Name the Baby!

Use the clues to complete this crossword puzzle.

ACROSS
1 A cow's baby is a _____.
4 A duck's baby is a _____.
6 A deer's baby is a _____.

DOWN
1 A bird's baby is a _____.
2 A dog's baby is a _____.
3 A cat's baby is a _____.
5 A sheep's baby is a _____.

Answer Page

ACROSS

1 A cow's baby is a __________.
4 A duck's baby is a __________.
6 A deer's baby is a __________.

DOWN

1 A bird's baby is a __________.
2 A dog's baby is a __________.
3 A cat's baby is a __________.
5 A sheep's baby is a __________.

1 CALF
4 DUCKLING
6 FAWN
1 CHICK
2 PUPPY
3 KITTEN
5 LAMB

I'm Hungry

Put the main ingredient of each food item
in the crossword puzzle below.

across
1 Guacamole
2 Salad

DOWN
3 Chicken cordon bleu
4 BLT
5 Lasagna
6 Omelet

ANSWER ON BACK

Answer Page

ACROSS
1 Guacamole
2 Salad

DOWN
3 Chicken cordon bleu
4 BLT
5 Lasagna
6 Omelet

Body Language

Use the pictures below to complete this crossword puzzle.

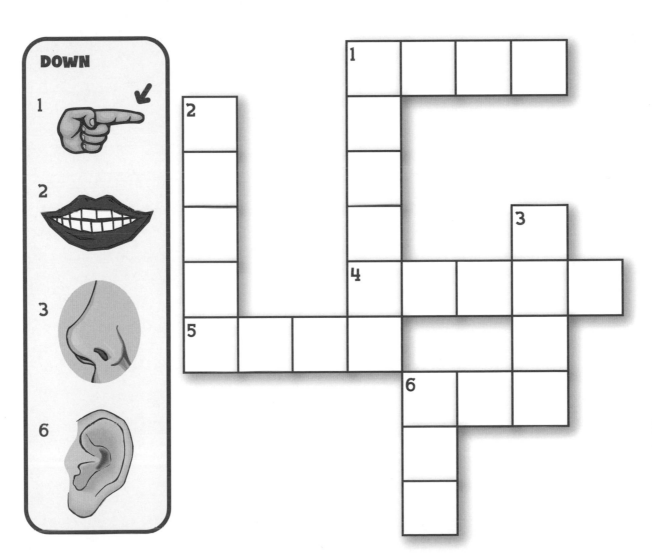

Answer Page

ACROSS

1. FOOT
4. ELBOW
5. HAIR
6. EYE

DOWN

1. FINGER
2. MOUTH
3. NOSE
6. EAR

In the City

Use the clues to complete this crossword puzzle.

ACROSS
2 These are the tall buildings found in cities.

4 A car that is often yellow in color and takes passengers where they need to go

DOWN
1 This sound may be heard from cars stuck in traffic jams.

3 An underground form of transportation found in many cities

Answer Page

ACROSS
2 These are the tall buildings found in cities.

4 A car that is often yellow in color and takes passengers where they need to go

DOWN
1 This sound may be heard from cars stuck in traffic jams.

3 An underground form of transportation found in many cities

¹B
E
²S K Y ³S C R A P E R S
U
B
W
⁴T A X I
Y

Class Schedule

Put the school subjects of each topic in the crossword puzzle below.

ACROSS
1 Latitude/longitude
2 Expressionism
3 Pythagorean Theorem

DOWN
4 Sonnet
5 War of 1812
6 Empirical charts

Answer Page

ACROSS	DOWN
1 Latitude/longitude	4 Sonnet
2 Expressionism	5 War of 1812
3 Pythagorean Theorem	6 Empirical charts

GEOGRAPHY
ENGLISH
HISTORY
ART
CHEMISTRY
MATH

Anatomically Correct!

Use the clues to complete this crossword puzzle.

ACROSS

2 You use these to chew your food.

4 We wrap these around people when giving hugs.

6 These help you see things.

7 We use these to pick up things and wave hello.

DOWN

1 This grumbles when you are hungry.

3 This covers your whole body and helps keep you warm.

5 These two extremities help you stand, run, and walk.

ANSWER ON BACK

Answer Page

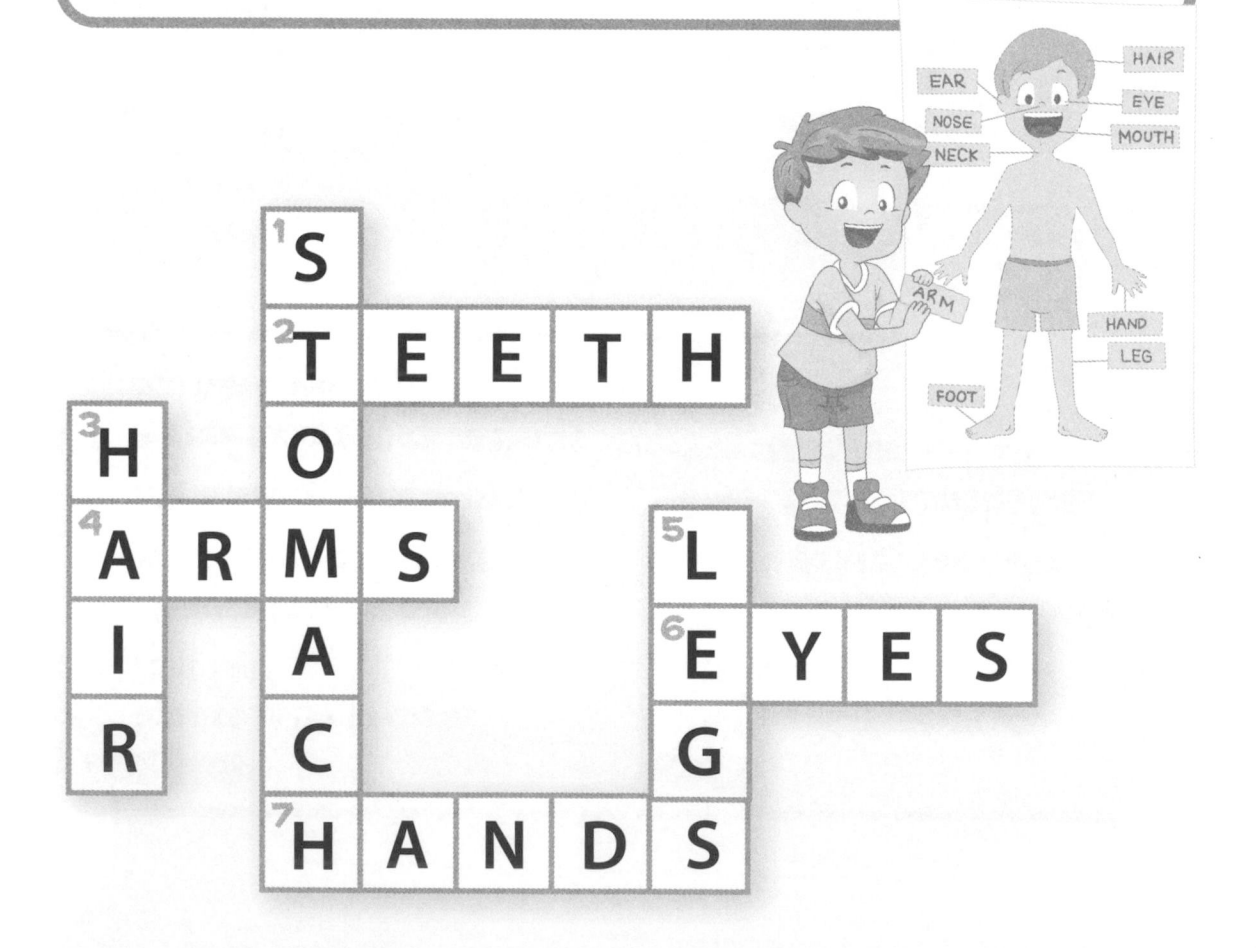

What in Your Room Am I?

Use the clues to complete this crossword puzzle.

across
2 I light up your room when you flip a switch.

5 I have drawers to keep your clothes organized.

DOWN
1 You can hang your clothes in me.

3 You sleep on me.

4 You can write and do your homework on top of my surface.

ANSWER ON BACK

Answer Page

across

2 I light up your room when you flip a switch.

5 I have drawers to keep your clothes organized.

DOWN

1 You can hang your clothes in me.

3 You sleep on me.

4 You can write and do your homework on top of my surface.

Let's Dance!

Unscramble these ballet terms on the blanks below and then place them in the crossword puzzle.

across

1 ITPOEN

_____

2 ELRANILAB

_____

3 AQEESRABU

_____

4 EEELVR

_____

DOWN

5 RERAB

_____

6 ETEJ

_____

7 RIPETTEUO

_____

8 ILEP

_____

Answer Page

ACROSS
1 ITPOEN
2 ELRANILAB
3 AQEESRABU
4 EELVR

DOWN
5 RERAB
6 ETEJ
7 RIPETTEUO
8 ILEP

Let's Build!

Unscramble these construction vehicles on the blanks below and then place them in the crossword puzzle.

ACROSS
1 MTUKCUPDR
_____
2 XVTREAAOC
_____

DOWN
1 GGREDI
_____
3 XRMEI
_____
4 LLREUBZDO
_____
5 TKFFLKOIR
_____

ANSWER ON BACK

Answer Page

across
1 MTUKCUPDR
2 XVTREAAOC

DOWN
1 GGREDI
3 XRMEI
4 LLREUBZDO
5 TKFFLKOIR

Crossword answers:

Across: 1 DUMPTRUCK, 2 EXCAVATOR

Down: 1 DIGGER, 3 MIXER, 4 BULLDOZER, 5 FORKLIFT

Where Am I?

Use the clues below to complete this crossword puzzle.

ACROSS
3 Circling
5 Hidden in back of
6 In the middle
7 Beneath

DOWN
1 Not indoors
2 Enter the building
4 Above
6 Next to

Answer Page

Jewelry

Use the clues to complete this crossword puzzle.

across

2 This is shown off on your neck and can be long or short.

3 This decorative jewelry is worn on your wrist.

4 You wear this on your finger.

DOWN

1 These come in pairs and can be studs, hoops, or dangly.

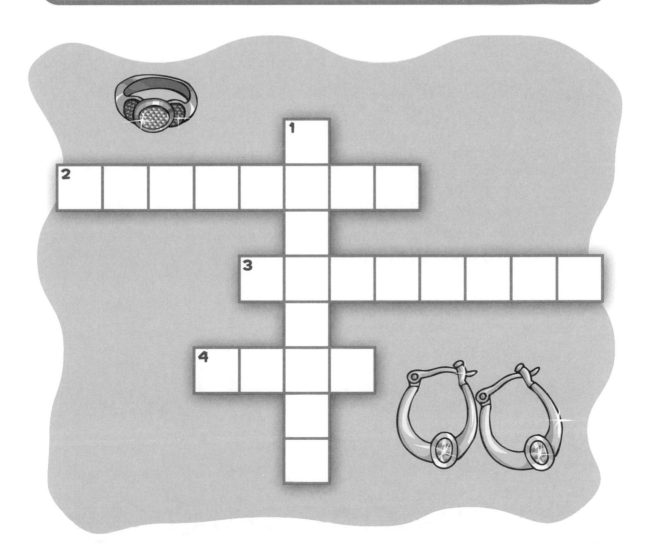

Answer Page

across

2 This is shown off on your neck and can be long or short.

3 This decorative jewelry is worn on your wrist.

4 You wear this on your finger.

DOWN

1 These come in pairs and can be studs, hoops, or dangly.

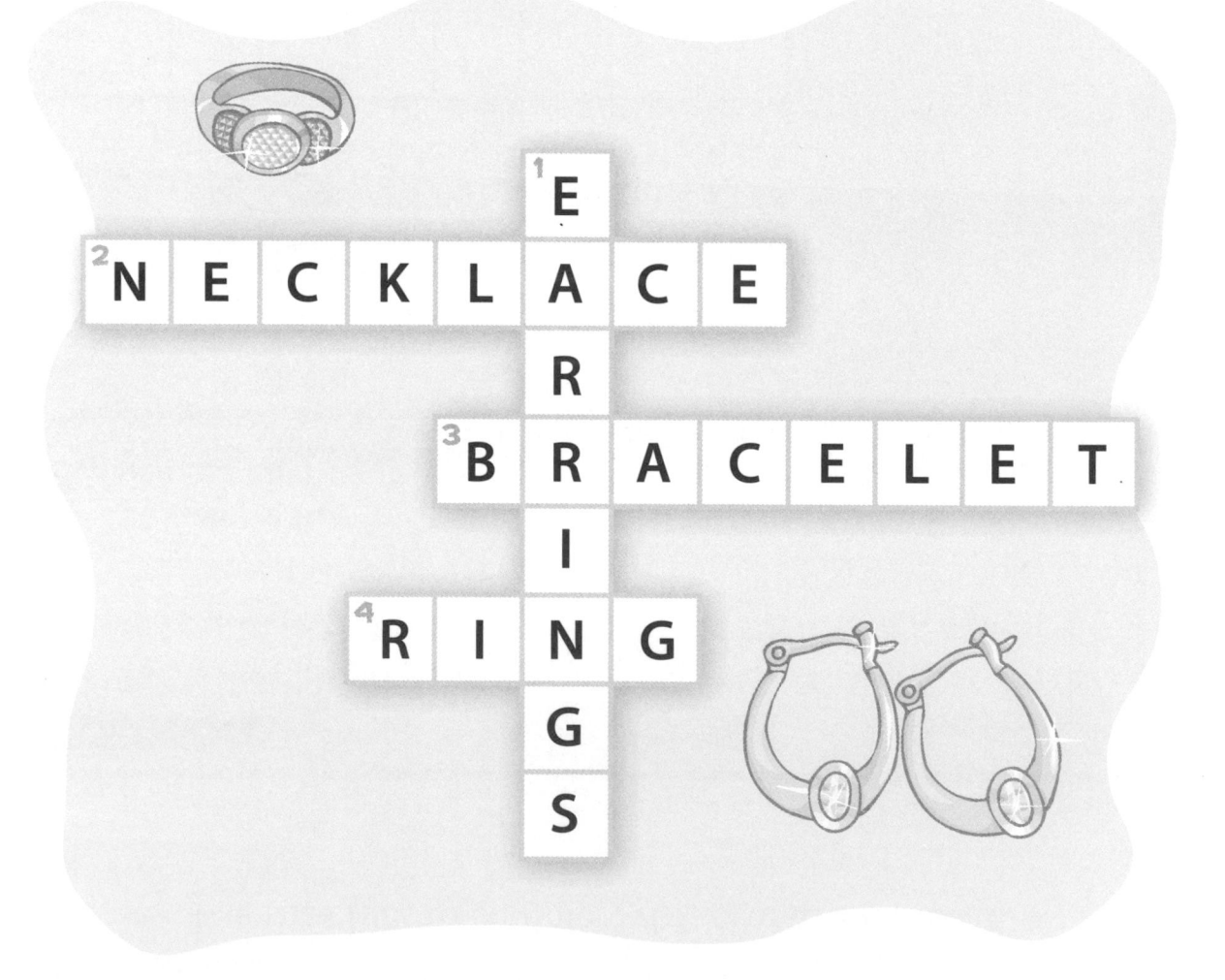

Building a House

Use the clues below to complete this crossword puzzle.

ACROSS
2 Outdoor room
4 Covers it all
6 Can cover the wall or floor
9 Lowest level
10 Keeps you warm
11 Hang out here
12 Open, close, see through

DOWN
1 Walk right through
3 Separates rooms
5 Cook up a meal here
7 Part of the roof
8 Where people sleep

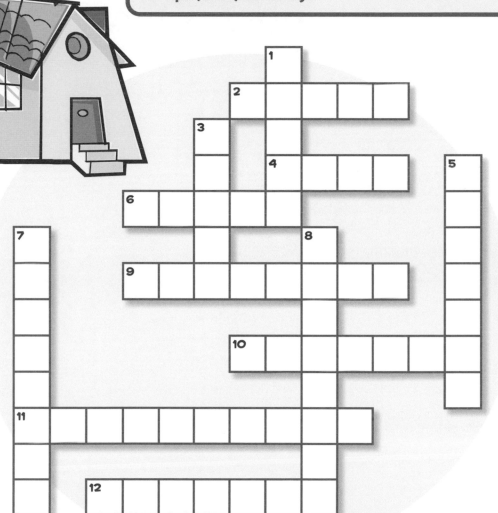

Answer Page

across
2 Outdoor room
4 Covers it all
6 Can cover the wall or floor
9 Lowest level
10 Keeps you warm
11 Hang out here
12 Open, close, see through

DOWN
1 Walk right through
3 Separates rooms
5 Cook up a meal here
7 Part of the roof
8 Where people sleep

Across:
2. PORCH
4. ROOF
6. TILES
9. BASEMENT
10. FURNACE
11. LIVINGROOM
12. WINDOWS

Down:
1. DOOR
3. WALL
5. KITCHEN
7. SHINGLES
8. BEDROOM

Subtract This!

Answer the subtraction problems below to complete this crossword puzzle.

ACROSS
1 100 - 50 =
2 60 - 40 =

DOWN
3 20 - 12 =
4 19 - 9 =

Answer Page

ACROSS
1 100 - 50 = 50
2 60 - 40 = 20

DOWN
3 20 - 12 = 8
4 19 - 9 = 10

Bath Time

Use the clues to complete this crossword puzzle.

ACROSS
2 This yellow rubber toy can float and squeak with you in the bathtub.

4 This sudsy substance is used to wash your hair.

DOWN
1 These can be added to a bath for some soapy fun!

3 You can lather your body with this to get rid of dirt.

Answer Page

Crossword solution:

1 B
2 D U C K
B
B
L
E
3 S
S O A
4 S H A M P O O

First Aid

Use the clues to complete this crossword puzzle.

ACROSS

1 This vehicle has a siren and transports sick or injured people to a hospital.

5 People go to this place when they are very sick.

6 This person works in a doctor's office or hospital and takes patients' blood pressure and temperature, among many other things.

DOWN

2 These help people walk when they can't bear weight on a foot or leg.

3 This is put on a broken arm or leg to immobilize it.

4 Doctors look at this image to see if a bone is broken.

Answer Page

ACROSS

1 This vehicle has a siren and transports sick or injured people to a hospital.

5 People go to this place when they are very sick.

6 This person works in a doctor's office or hospital and takes patients' blood pressure and temperature, among many other things.

DOWN

2 These help people walk when they can't bear weight on a foot or leg.

3 This is put on a broken arm or leg to immobilize it.

4 Doctors look at this image to see if a bone is broken.

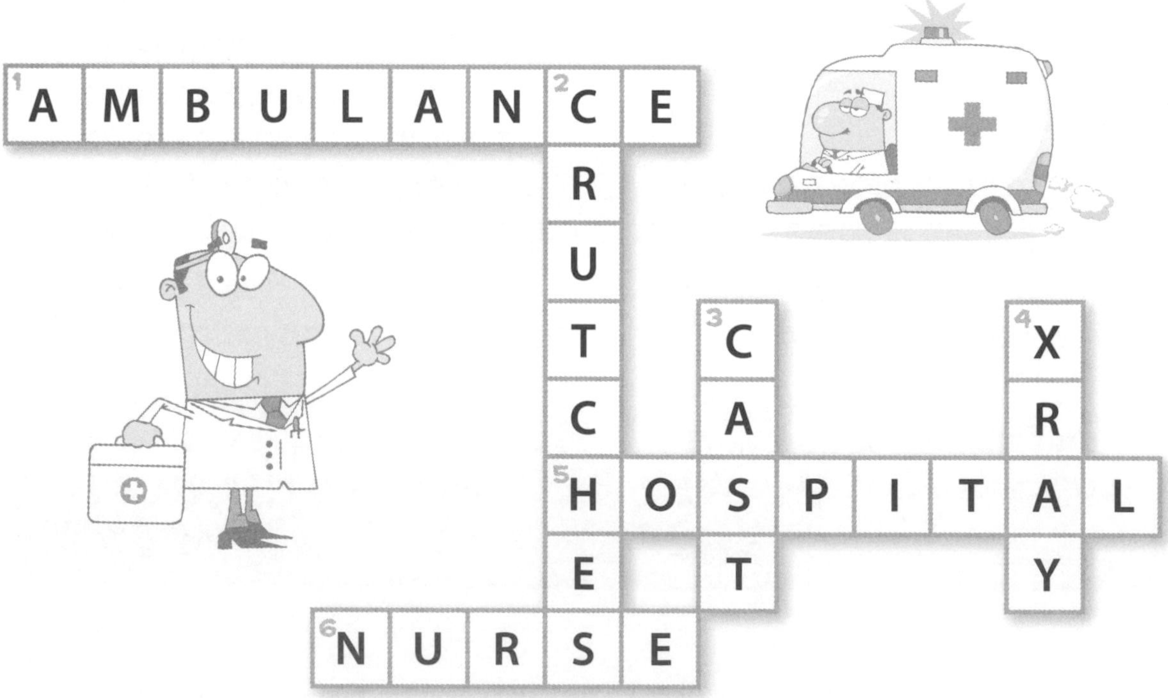

1 AMBULANCE
2 CRUTCHES
3 CAST
4 XRAY
5 HOSPITAL
6 NURSE

Music to Your Ears

Use the pictures below to complete this crossword puzzle.

ANSWER ON BACK

Answer Page

Let's Go Camping

Use the clues to complete this crossword puzzle.

across

2 This magnetic instrument will keep you from getting lost.

3 These types of stories are told around the campfire to spook people.

4 You may need this device to see at night when you are walking in the dark.

5 This temporary outdoor structure has a zipper for a door.

6 You will want to curl up into this type of bag at night to keep warm until morning.

DOWN

1 To make s'mores, this sweet confection is sandwiched with marshmallows in between two graham crackers.

2 This is used for cooking, roasting marshmallows, and keeping campsites warm.

ANSWER ON BACK

Answer Page

across

2 This magnetic instrument will keep you from getting lost.

3 These types of stories are told around the campfire to spook people.

4 You may need this device to see at night when you are walking in the dark.

5 This temporary outdoor structure has a zipper for a door.

6 You will want to curl up into this type of bag at night to keep warm until morning.

DOWN

1 To make s'mores, this sweet confection is sandwiched with marshmallows in between two graham crackers.

2 This is used for cooking, roasting marshmallows, and keeping campsites warm.

All Sports

Use the pictures below to complete this crossword puzzle.

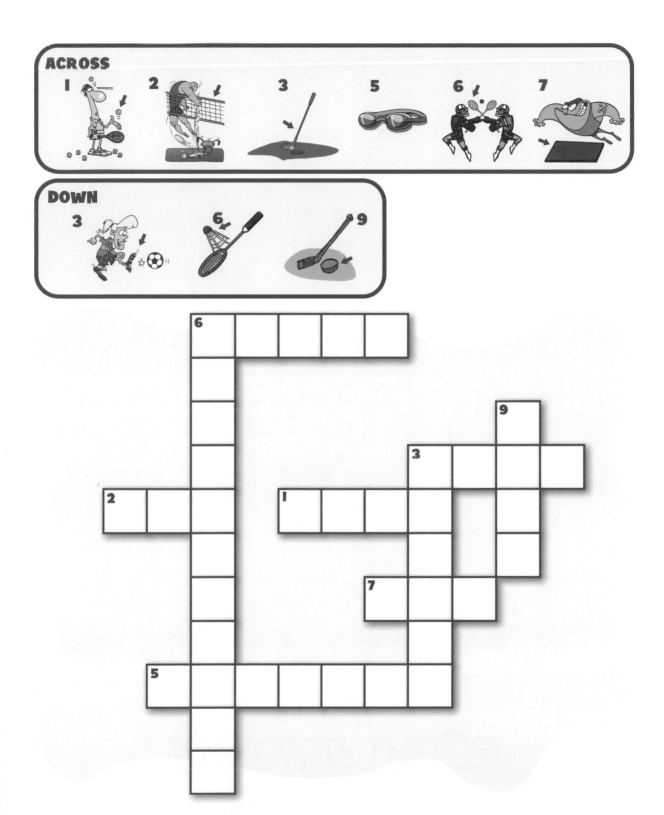

Answer Page

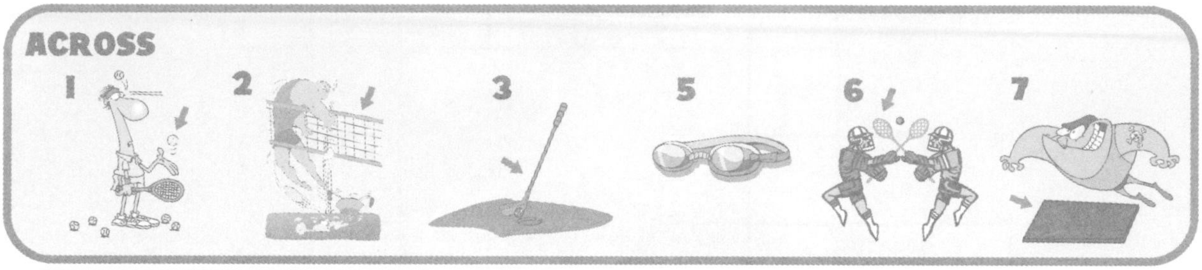
ACROSS
1
2
3
5
6
7

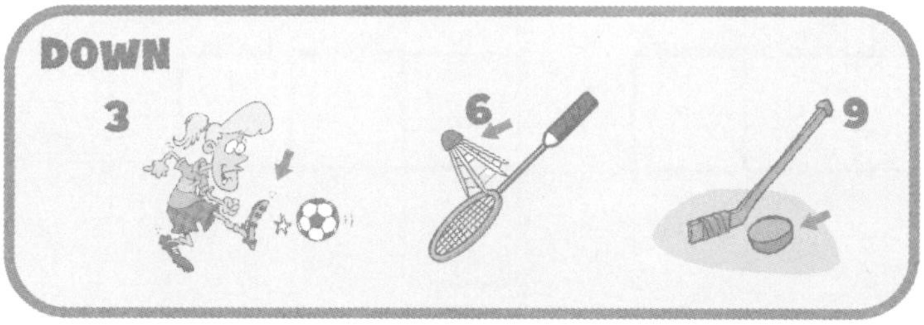
DOWN
3
6
9

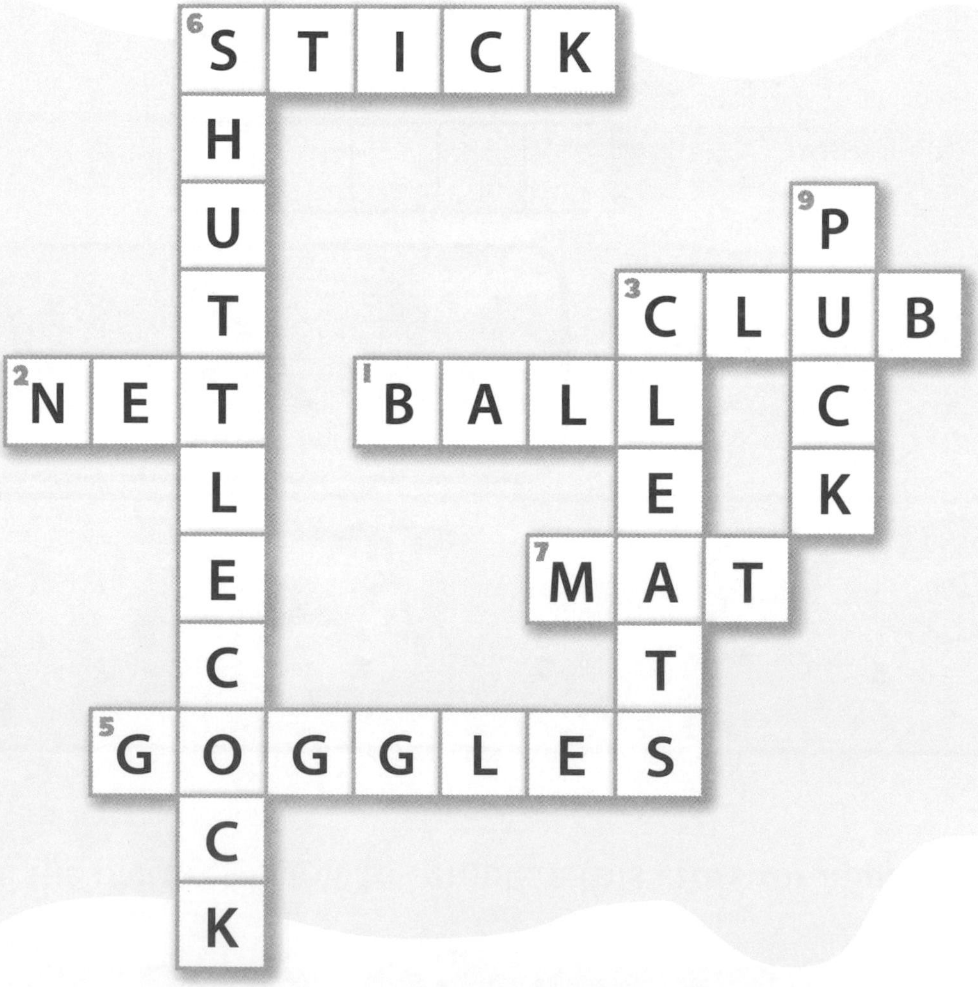
6 STICK
6 SHUTTLECOCK
2 NET
1 BALL
3 CLUB
3 CLEATS
9 PUCK
7 MAT
5 GOGGLES

Time to Laugh!

Use the clues below to complete this crossword puzzle.

ACROSS
2 Little laugh
7 ____—____ who's there?
8 Silly questions and answers

DOWN
1 Show your teeth
3 Animated shows
4 In the circus
5 Stand-up guy
6 Tell me funny ones

Answer Page

ACROSS

2 Little laugh
7 _____ — _____ who's there?
8 Silly questions and answers

DOWN

1 Show your teeth
3 Animated shows
4 In the circus
5 Stand-up guy
6 Tell me funny ones

								¹S		
								M		
²C	H	U	³C	K	L	E		I		
			A					L		
⁴C		⁵C	R					E		
L		O	T							
O		M	O				⁶J			
W		I	O				O			
⁷K	N	O	C	K	K	N	O	C	K	
			N				K			
			S				E			
⁸R	I	D	D	L	E	S				

In The Cupboard

Match up the missing word in these "serving" phrases
to complete this crossword puzzle.

ACROSS
1 ___ and fork
2 Glass of ___

DOWN
3 Soup ___
4 ___ pan

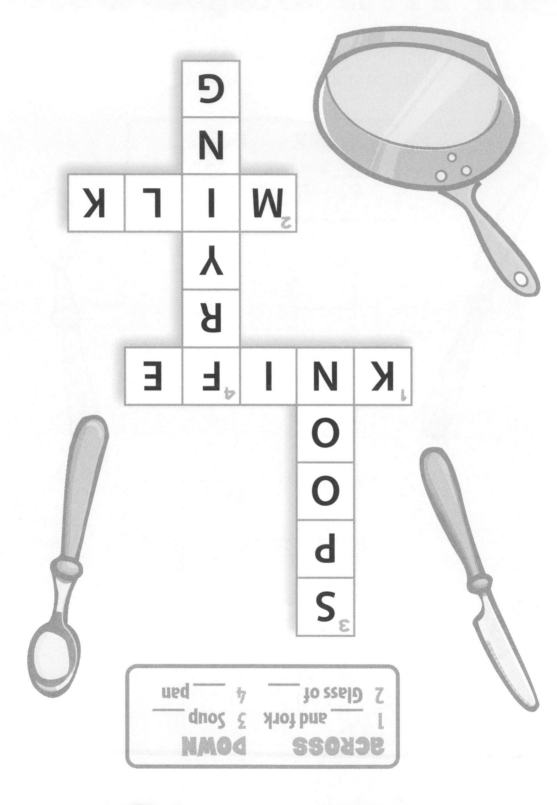

DRYING

MILK

KNIFE

SPOONS

ACROSS
1 ___ and fork
2 Glass of ___

DOWN
3 Soup ___
4 ___ pan

Answer Page

Breakfast Food

Use the clues to complete this crossword puzzle.

ACROSS

3 I go great with cream cheese or butter.

4 I can be brown or white and you use me to make an omelet.

6 You can flip me in the air to turn me over before serving me with butter and syrup.

DOWN

1 I am round, sweet, and am often covered with frosting and sprinkles.

2 I can be cooked in a special iron, made just for me!

5 I am a favorite breakfast juice and can be prepared with or without pulp.

Answer Page

across

3 I go great with cream cheese or butter.

4 I can be brown or white and you use me to make an omelet.

6 You can flip me in the air to turn me over before serving me with butter and syrup.

DOWN

1 I am round, sweet, and am often covered with frosting and sprinkles.

2 I can be cooked in a special iron, made just for me!

5 I am a favorite breakfast juice and can be prepared with or without pulp.

You Won!

Use the clues to complete this crossword puzzle.

ACROSS

1 In swimming or horseback riding, participants try to win a first place blue_____.

4 In sports like soccer and hockey, players try to score as many_____ as they can to win.

5 Sometimes a game can end with both teams having the same score, that's called a ____.

6 In the Olympics, athletes hope to win the gold_____.

DOWN

2 In this sport, players score points by dunking orange balls into _____.

3 In baseball, when a player hits the ball out of the park it is called a _____ run.

ANSWER ON BACK

Answer Page

ACROSS

1 In swimming or horseback riding, participants try to win a first place blue________.

4 In sports like soccer and hockey, players try to score as many_______ as they can to win.

5 Sometimes a game can end with both teams having the same score, that's called a _____.

6 In the Olympics, athletes hope to win the gold_______.

DOWN

2 In this sport, players score points by dunking orange balls into _________.

3 In baseball, when a player hits the ball out of the park it is called a _______ run.

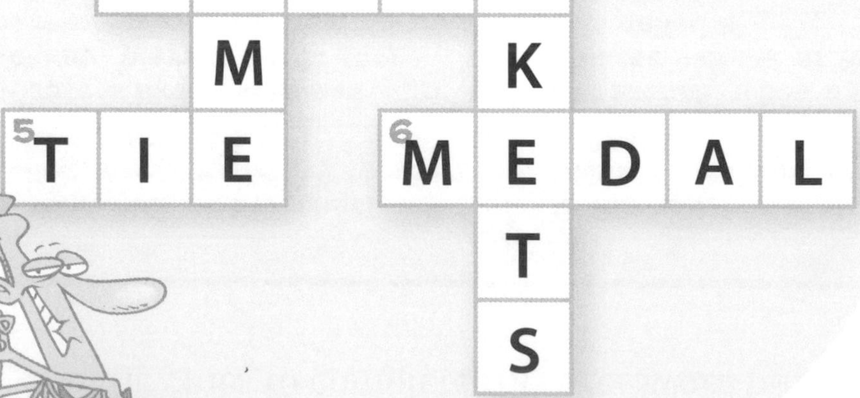

1 RIBBON
2 BASKETS
3 HOME
4 GOALS
5 TIE
6 MEDAL

Flowers

Use the clues to complete this crossword puzzle.

across

3 A very large yellow flower that produces edible seeds

5 This is someone who sells flowers.

DOWN

1 This is an arrangement of flowers often carried by brides and bridesmaids.

2 These flowers are a symbol of romance and are often purchased by the dozen.

4 A flower with white petals and a yellow center

ANSWER ON BACK

Answer Page

ACROSS

3 A very large yellow flower that produces edible seeds

5 This is someone who sells flowers.

DOWN

1 This is an arrangement of flowers often carried by brides and bridesmaids.

2 These flowers are a symbol of romance and are often purchased by the dozen.

4 A flower with white petals and a yellow center

Crossword solution:
- 5 FLORIST
- 4 DAISY
- 3 SUNFLOWER
- 1 BOUQUET
- 2 ROSES

Fun at the Park

Use the pictures below to complete this crossword puzzle.

Answer Page

Across

1 JUMPROPE

2 MONKEYBARS

Down

3 TRICYCLE

4 SWING

Rocking Out!

Use the clues below to complete this crossword puzzle.

ACROSS

1 The people who buy the tickets and cheer on the performers

3 The music group who performs

4 A musical performance at an arena

DOWN

2 The person in the band whose voice is his or her instrument

5 What you need to be admitted to a concert

Answer Page

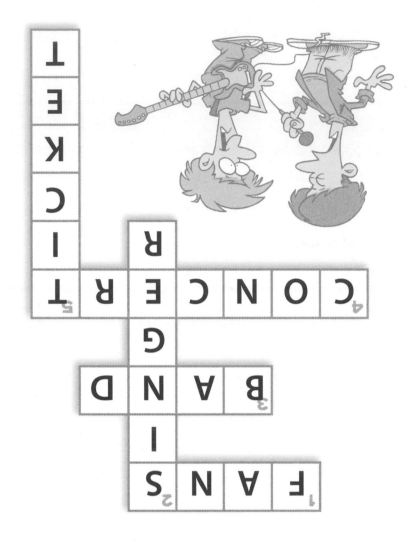

ACROSS

1 The people who buy the tickets and cheer on the performers
3 The music group who performs
4 A musical performance at an arena

DOWN

2 The person in the band whose voice is his or her instrument
5 What you need to be admitted to a concert

Landmarks

Use the clues below to complete this crossword puzzle.

ACROSS

2 Forever crooked, this Italian building, the _____ Tower of Pisa, is a favorite tourist attraction.

4 In Australia, fish and other sea creatures live in this huge underwater area called the Great Barrier_____.

5 The most famous clock in London is called Big _____.

6 Paris's most famous landmark is called the Eiffel _____.

DOWN

1 In Rome, Italy, gladiators used to battle inside the _____.

3 In Asia, the nearly 5,500 mile-long stone structure built to protect the Chinese Empire is called the _____ Wall of China.

Answer Page

ACROSS

2 Forever crooked, this Italian building, the _____ Tower of Pisa, is a favorite tourist attraction.

4 In Australia, fish and other sea creatures live in this huge underwater area called the Great Barrier_____.

5 The most famous clock in London is called Big _____.

6 Paris's most famous landmark is called the Eiffel _____.

DOWN

1 In Rome, Italy, gladiators used to battle inside the _____.

3 In Asia, the nearly 5,500 mile-long stone structure built to protect the Chinese Empire is called the _____ Wall of China.

COLISSEUM

LEANING

GREAT

REEF

BEN

TOWER

At the Circus

Use the clues below to complete this crossword puzzle.

ACROSS

4 A circus is usually set inside one of these.

5 This type of cake is deep-fried and covered in powdered sugar.

6 This person is in charge of all the acts in the circus.

DOWN

1 A man or woman at the circus tames this large, roaring animal.

2 Circus performers sometimes ride this enormous animal.

3 These are funny people with big red noses and colorful hair.

4 Acrobats swing back and forth on this bar held up by two ropes.

Answer Page

aCROSS

4 A circus is usually set inside one of these.

6 This person is in charge of all the acts in the circus.

5 This type of cake is deep-fried and covered in powdered sugar.

DOWN

1 A man or woman at the circus tames this large, roaring animal.

2 Circus performers sometimes ride this enormous animal.

3 These are funny people with big red noses and colorful hair.

4 Acrobats swing back and forth on this bar held up by two ropes.

Crossword grid answers:

- TENT
- TRAPEZE
- ELEPHANT
- RINGMASTER
- CLOWNS
- FUNNEL
- LION

Party Time

Use the pictures below to complete this crossword puzzle.

ACROSS

3   5   7   8

DOWN

1   2   4   6

Answer Page

ACROSS

3 5 7 8

DOWN

1 2 4 6

Surfing Safari

Use the clues below to complete this crossword puzzle.

ACROSS

2 This is what surfers ride to get "tubed!"

3 This is the long floating device used for surfing.

4 Some surfers hang these ten digits off their boards.

DOWN

1 Surfers look like black seals when they're wearing one of these to keep warm.

2 When a surfer falls off the board into the waves, its called a _____.

Answer Page

across

2 This is what surfers ride to get "tubed!"

3 This is the long floating device used for surfing.

4 Some surfers hang these ten digits off their boards.

DOWN

1 Surfers look like black seals when they're wearing one of these to keep warm.

2 When a surfer falls off the board into the waves, its called a _____.

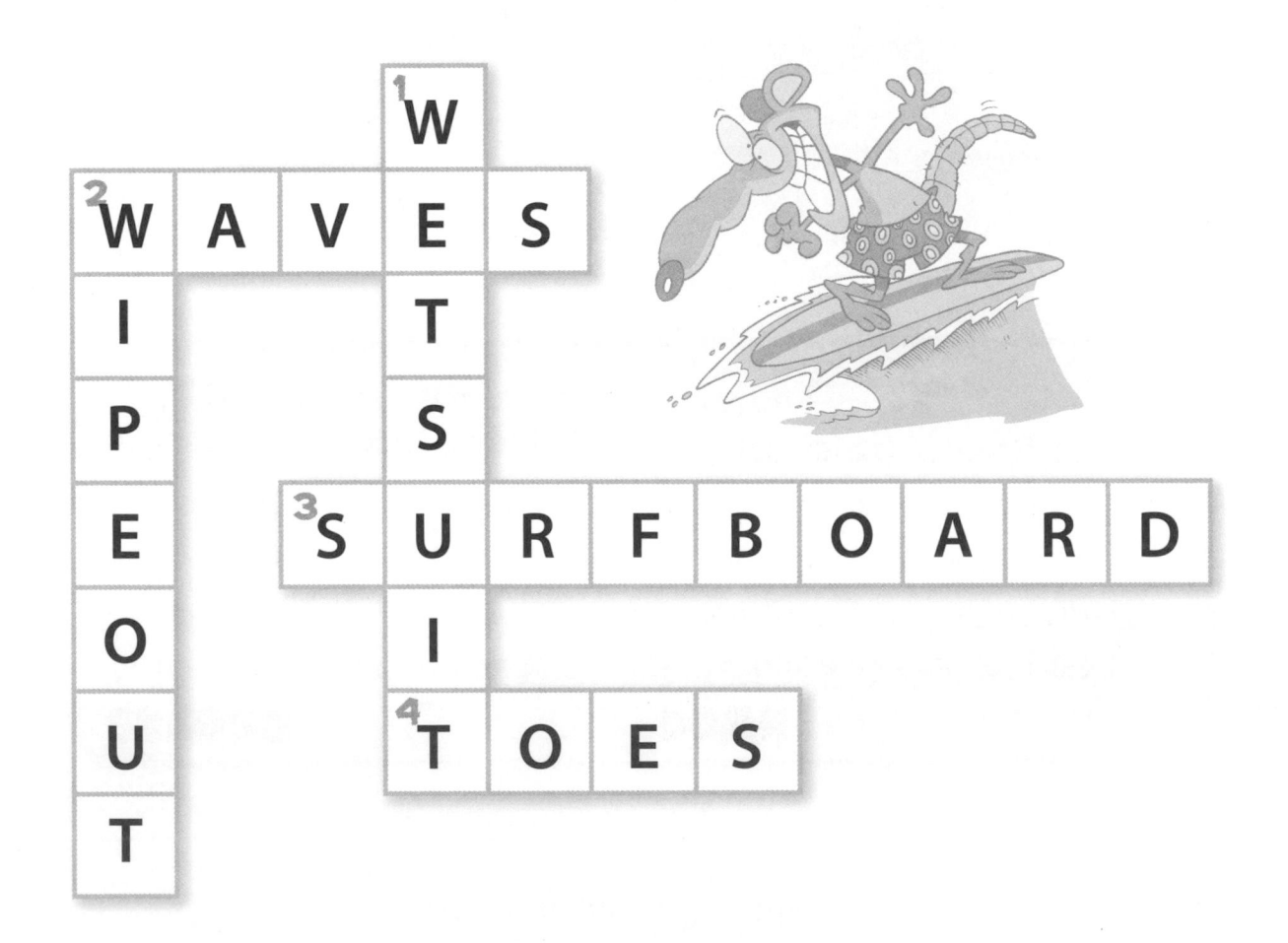

Have a Seat

Use the clues below to complete this crossword puzzle.

ACROSS

1 Most dining rooms have these seats around the table.

4 This sacklike comfy chair gets its name from small legumes.

DOWN

2 Some desk chairs do this so the person sitting in one can turn around without getting up.

3 Also called a couch, this is a long, comfortable place to sit.

Answer Page

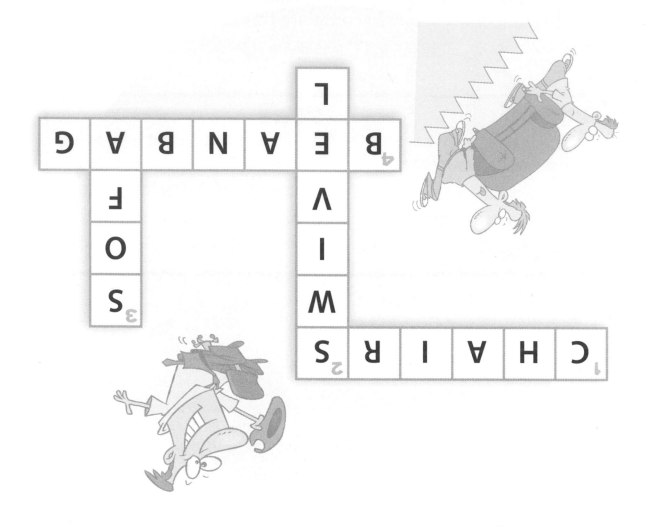

Grid answers: BEANBAG, SOFA, CHAIRS, SWIVEL

ACROSS

1 Most dining rooms have these seats around the table.

4 This sacklike comfy chair gets its name from small legumes.

DOWN

2 Some desk chairs do this so the person sitting in one can turn around without getting up.

3 Also called a couch, this is a long, comfortable place to sit.

What Shape Am I?

Put the shape of each picture in the crossword puzzle below.

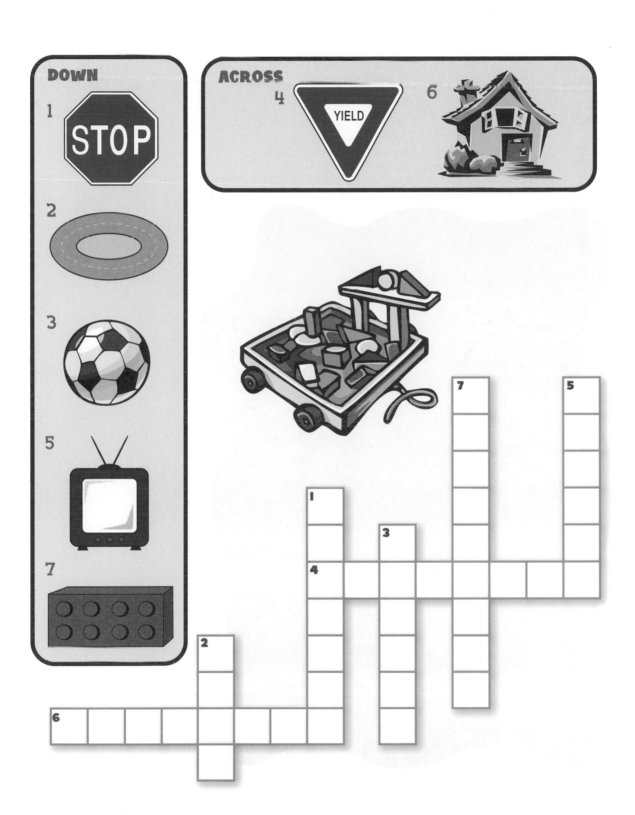

DOWN

1

2

3

5

7

ACROSS

4   YIELD   6

Answer Page

DOWN

1

2

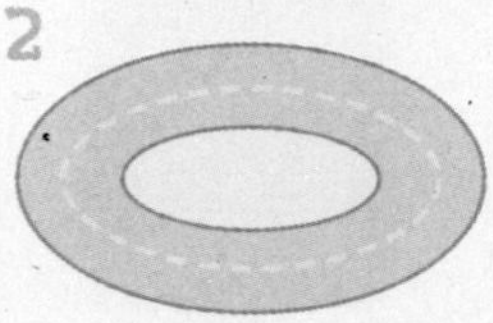

3

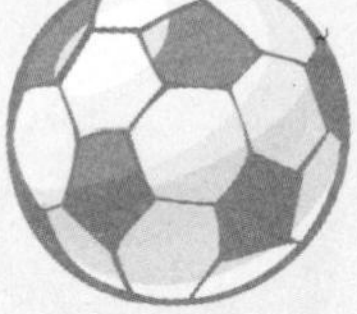

5

7

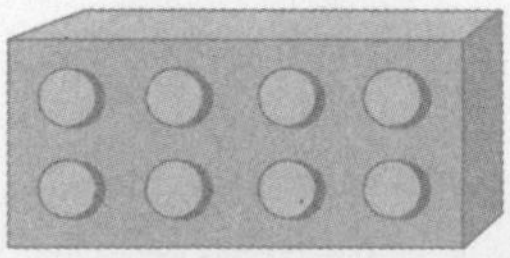

ACROSS

4

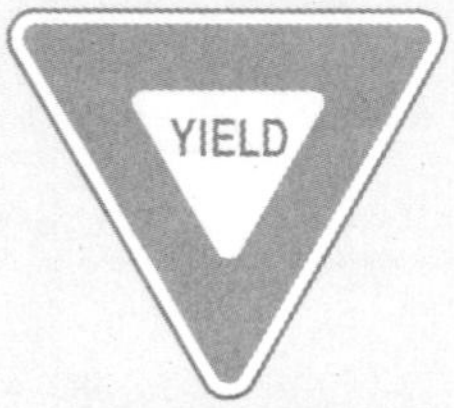

6

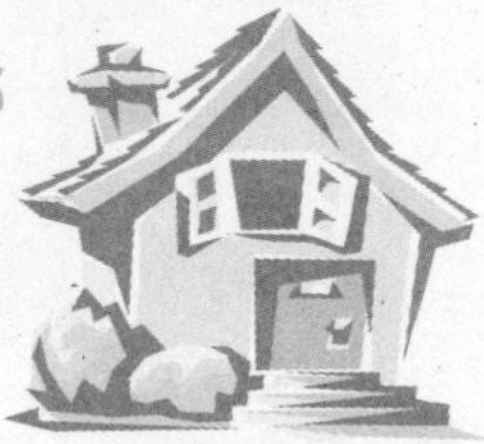

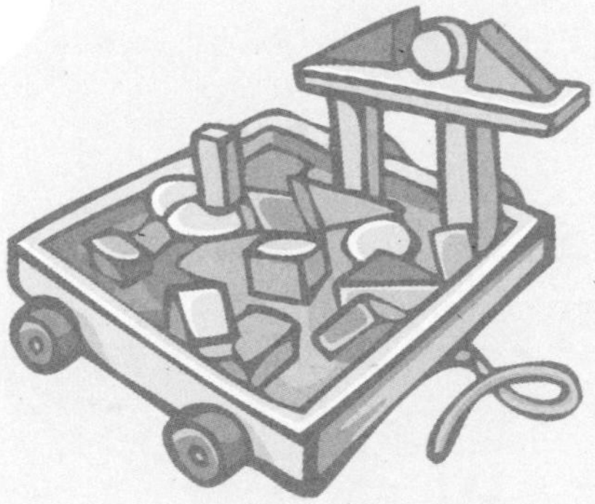

1 OCTAGON
2 OVAL
3 CIRCLE
4 TRIANGLE
5 SQUARE
6 PENTAGON
7 RECTANGLE

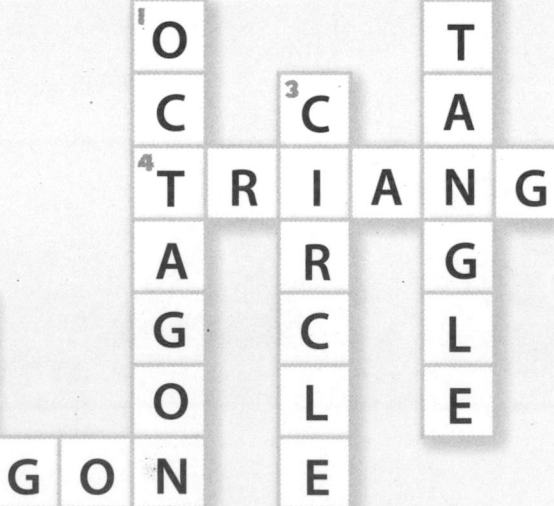